3.102

PLANT LAYOUT

A Guide to the Layout of Process Plant and Sites

J. C. Mecklenburgh

Department of Chemical Engineering
University of Nottingham

Leonard Hill Books   in association with The Institution of
An Intertext Publisher   Chemical Engineers

Published by
Leonard Hill Books
a division of
International Textbook Company Limited
24 Market Square,
Aylesbury, Bucks HP20 1TL.

First published 1973

ISBN 0 249 44125 X

Photoset in Malta by St Paul's Press Ltd
Printed in Great Britain by
Billing & Sons Ltd., Guildford and London

ACKNOWLEDGEMENTS

Prepared 1969/72 for the Engineering Practice Committee of the Institution of Chemical Engineers by the following Working Party

Chairman
Dr J. C. Mecklenburgh, University of Nottingham

Members
Mr K. A. Beckett, Imperial Chemical Industries Ltd (Organics Division), Manchester
Mr L. Blakeborough, Whessoe Project Engineers Ltd, Darlington (to 1970)
Mr J. McN. Bruce, British Steel Corporation, Rotherham
Mr J. Madden, Isopipe Limited, Nottingham (formerly Courtaulds Ltd, Derby)
Mr E. S. Swan, Woodall-Duckham Ltd, Crawley
Dr G. L. Wells, University of Sheffield

Corresponding Members
Mr W. E. Bryden, Consultant, Lundin Links, Scotland
Mr P. Crombie, Industrial Planning and Engineering Co—Life Ltd, Israel.
Mr E. Holmes, Consultant, Huddersfield
Mr J. A. Holman, BP Chemicals Limited, London

The Working Party thanks numerous other individuals and companies who provided material and comments. Also thanks to Miss P. J. Kelham for so patiently typing and re-typing the numerous drafts.

LIST OF CONTENTS

Acknowledgements iii
List of Illustrations vii
List of Tables ix
Introduction xi

Part I

1 Site Layout 3

1.1 General 3
1.2 Material transportation 6
1.3 Location of services 7
1.4 Effluent 9
1.5 Central buildings 10
1.6 Access 11
1.7 Emergency services 12
1.8 Environmental aspects 13
1.9 Geographical factors 14

2 Plant Layout 15

2.1 General 15
2.2 Buildings 21

3 Techniques for Layout 28

3.1 The principles of layout development 28
3.2 Details of techniques for layout 29
3.3 Layout analogues 43
3.4 Computers 53

4 Appendix to Part I 56

4.1 Typical areas and sizes for preliminary site layouts 56
4.2 Typical clearances between various units for preliminary
site layouts 57
4.3 Typical constraint allowances for preliminary plant layout 58

Part II

1 Layout of Plant Items   63

   1.1 Plant vessels   63
   1.2 Furnaces and fired equipment   72
   1.3 Columns   73
   1.4 Exchangers   75
   1.5 Fluid transfer equipment   78
   1.6 Filters   83
   1.7 Centrifuges   86
   1.8 Dryers and similar gas–solid contactors   86
   1.9 Mills and crushers   91
   1.10 Screens   94
   1.11 Cyclones, air filters and precipitators   95
   1.12 Conveyors   98
   1.13 Specialised and packaged plants   101

2 Layout of Storage   102

   2.1 Liquid storage   102
   2.2 Gas and pressure storage   109
   2.3 Bulk solids storage   109
   2.4 Filling and packaging equipment   118
   2.5 Warehouse storage   120

3 Layout of Pipework   122

   3.1 Pipes   122
   3.2 Pipe fittings   130

References   135
Index to Clearances, Sizes etc.   143
Subject Index   146

LIST OF ILLUSTRATIONS

1 Diagram of flow of products through petrochemical site super-
  imposed on site layout 4
2 Typical site layout 5
3 Construction access 19
4 Stair and fixed ladder layout 24
5 Control building layout 27
6 Typical control panel layout 27
7 Heights of instruments 28
8 Typical plant layout and design network 31
9 Process chart 39
10 Grid showing absolute exclusions 40
11 Grid showing permissible layouts 41
12 Exchanger cut-out 44
13 Overlapping of cut-outs 44
14 Block layout model 45
15 Typical site layout drawing 47
16 Typical plot plan 48
17 Typical layout elevation 49
18 Piping model 51
19 Access to reactors 65
20 Moving bed column showing conveyor 67
21 Layout of multi-effect evaporators 71
22 Typical distillation column layout 76
23 Grouping of exchangers 77
24 Layout of main pump bay allowing ready access for
  inspection and maintenance 80
25 Compressor layout 82
26 Fans on a gas reformer plant 83
27 Layout of rotary vacuum filter 85
28 Rotary cylinder dryer explosion chamber 87
29 Anhydro spray dryer in anhydro laboratory 88
30 Pneumatic conveyor dryer with cyclone 89
31 Operations in tray drying 90
32 Typical layout in hammer-mill house 92
33 Suspended magnet 93
34 Magnetic pulley 93
35 Sizing samples 95

36 Bag filter installation   96
37 Electrostatic precipitators   96
38 Typical troughed belt conveyor   97
39 Typical chute detail   97
40 Typical supporting gantries for 750mm wide belt conveyors   99
41 Typical cross-section through a fluidised gravity conveyor   100
42 Inert gas generators   101
43 Cell house for reductive dimerisation of acrylonitrile   101
44 Typical tank farm layout   103
45 Variable multi-storage layout   108
46 Single conical open stockpile fed by belt conveyor   112
47 Typical drag scraper scheme   113
48 Large open stockpile fed by travelling tripper conveyor   114
49 Warehouse-type materials store   115
50 Typical layout of vertical silos   118
51 Packaging and filling line   119
52 Packaging booths   120
53 Warehouse unloading point   122
54 Typical palletised store   122
55 Distance on pipe bridges and racks   127
56 Layout on pipe racks   130
57 Access to pipe flanges   131
58 Valve height   132

LIST OF TABLES

1 Typical stages in plant layout 32
2 Critical examination sheet 34
3 Comparison of plot plans 36
4 Details for rigid chassis road tankers 104
5 Details for articulated road tankers 105
6 Typical spacings for liquid storage vessels 106
7 Liquid flammable gases: safety distances for location and spacing 110
8 Open pile storage 116
9 Approximate space requirements for closed warehouses 117
10 Examples of conventional (single) racking 123
11 Example of live storage 123
12 Example of outside palletised storage 123
13 Distance between centre lines of pipes in pipe-tracks and trenches for 1 and 2 MN/m² Class 126

INTRODUCTION

Layout is concerned with spatial arrangement and has a vital influence on the profitability of chemical and process plant. Good layout practice achieves an economic balance of the requirements of safety, the environment, construction, maintenance, operation, room for future expansion and of process relationships such as gravity flow or positive pump suction heads.

This work is intended as a guide to the achievement of good layout particularly for those who cannot draw on past experience either from their own career or from company manuals. It is in two parts. The first deals with general aspects of site and plant layout and with methods for preparing layouts. The second part contains information about detailed layout of individual plant items, pipework and storage. The information includes spacings and arrangements. It must be remembered though that these are only typical and may have to be altered to suit local conditions, clients' requirements and established safe practices. In particular a guide of this sort must invariably be phrased in terms of a new or 'greenfield' project whereas most situations are involved with modifications where the constraints make compromises of good practice almost inevitable.

Part I

1 SITE LAYOUT

1.1 General

Ideally before a site is selected a preliminary layout should be made. This should be based on the principle that the purpose of a good site layout is to provide safe and economical flow of materials and people. A materials flowsheet for the site is therefore prepared which then allows the various processes to be positioned relative to one another (see *Figure 1*). Next the services (e.g., boiler house, effluent plant etc) are added in the most convenient positions. The central buildings (administration, canteens, central workshops, laboratories) are placed so that the distances travelled by personnel to use them is minimised. Finally the road and rail systems are marked in. Typical sizes and clearances are given in the Appendix to Part I to aid the preliminary layout.

This preliminary layout then forms one of the criteria for site selection particularly for topographical and geological considerations. Other factors affecting site selection are product markets, raw material supplies, proximity to the national road, rail and port systems, availability of local labour, water and effluent facilities, scope for future expansion, governmental influences, and investment incentives.

After purchase the layout engineer has to adjust his plans to the constraints of the site. It is important that these constraints are clearly established. They could include:

1) Topographical, geological and meteorological conditions
2) Environmental conditions relating to adjacent properties
3) Site boundary and service parameters
    e.g. main and public roads
       railway entry
       oil, gas pipelines etc
       permitted storm water and sewage outfalls
       process and potable water supplies
       power supply

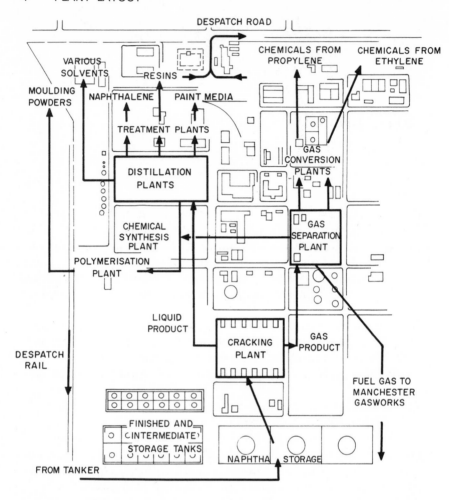

Figure 1   *Diagram of flow of products through petrochemical site super-imposed on site layout (by courtesy of H. E. Charlton, Manchester Association of Engineers.)*

4) Legal requirements
   e.g. planning and building laws and bye-laws
        effluent and pollution requirements
        traffic regulations
        fire and other safety requirements

Site standards should also be established such as:

Figure 2 *Typical site layout—fertilizer plant, Kuwait (by courtesy of Foster Wheeler Ltd.)*

1) Road width, radii, gradients, etc.
2) Service corridors
3) Pipe bridges (e.g. height over roads, railways)
4) Building lines
5) Architectural finish to buildings etc....

Having established site constraints and standards a more detailed site layout can be made. The same order of consideration as for the preliminary layout is taken, viz., process plant layout by material flow with the positions of the service utilities and administration buildings added afterwards. However the site constraints may make it easier to consider the position of the process plants after fixing the distribution of those utilities coming from off site (roads, railways, power supply, stormwater and sewage drainage, process and potable water). Services generated on site (steam plant, workshop, offices etc) can still be positioned after fixing the layout of the plants. The total layout should then be considered to see whether the layout is consistent with safety requirements and that it assists action in an emergency. Before completing the layout it should be checked to see that the constraints and standards have not been violated.

Careful consideration should be given to defining battery limits or areas of responsibility. The works should be provided with a security boundary fence and all entrances should be provided with a gatehouse. For security reasons the number of entrances should be kept to a minimum but when an extension is being built, this building site should have a separate entrance and gatehouse and its own boundary fence. In this way access for delivery of construction materials is kept clear of existing operating plant. The main works boundary fence may serve as part of this boundary but any gateway between the main works and the building site must have its own security control point.

When setting out a site it is essential to establish a site datum level. If the site is sufficiently large it may be necessary to have subsidiary bench marks from which all measurements can be made. A useful way of doing this is to lay down a base line at the side of roadways if these are at right angles. This enables a theodolite to be used from fixed points as well as determining bench marks, and ties in with a map grid.

References   See References 67–73 on Site Location and References 33–38 on General Layout.

1.2 Material Transportation

A good site layout minimises the distance materials have to flow either to or from store or during processing. It separates the raw material unloading facilities from the product loading areas. These two objectives can be met by first laying out the site in the same order as the site material flow diagram *(Figure 1)* and then refining and quantifying this layout by the techniques given in Part I Section 3. However, the result may have to be changed to accommodate other factors such as keeping the external raw material and product traffic away from all other traffic needed for engineering, canteen, construction, personnel. Another factor to accommodate is the isolation of hazardous operations which may need their own security fence. It is necessary in this respect to meet statutory and company regulations. It is not necessary that there should only be one unloading area, one storage area, etc. The numbers depend on, amongst other things, the range, throughputs and danger classifications of the raw materials and products and on the interaction between the various manufacturing processes.

Unloading and loading areas should be situated on the edge of the site near the point of entry (i.e. near the road entrances, rail spur or dock). However, if the materials are at all unpleasant or hazardous these areas cannot be near the entrance, although they can still be near the site boundary if inconvenience is not caused to neighbours. It is usual for the storage areas to be alongside the loading and unloading areas in order to control the positioning of materials in store. Ideally the plant should then be next to the store on the other side from the shipment area. Again this is not always possible or even desirable if hazardous materials are involved.

Internal transportation of materials can be by pipeline, conveyors, or vehicles. Pipelines should be run parallel to the road system in the same way as the utilities are distributed, in fact, pipe routes can be shared between chemicals and services. Where vehicles are used the routes they follow should be planned and, if necessary, bridges built where busy routes cross.

For details of layout of storage and loading areas, pipelines and conveyors, see Part II.

1.3 Location of Services

The boiler house, power station, cooling towers, switch and pumping stations, etc. should be located in positions where they will not be put out of action by fire or flood and so that the steam, water and electricity supply mains to the major consumers will not be uneconomically lengthy. Services may be on a periphery, but situated adjacent to the largest users. On the other hand, it may be preferable to put these services in the centre of the site, so that the plant can expand in all directions. Consideration needs to be given to a ring main system.

1.3.1 Boiler House and Power Station

In locating the boiler house, the effects of a troublesome or prevailing wind on the stack emission or of dust from the fuel pile should be taken into account. Direct access, avoiding the process areas, should be provided for the fuel supplies. Boiler water treatment plants are usually situated within the boiler house. However very large treatment plants may be contained in a separate building or area to permit access for regenerate chemicals and locating water storage and effluent drainage systems.

1.3.2 Cooling Towers

Cooling towers should be sited so that water drift will not restrict visibility or cause exterior corrosion or ice formation on other parts of the plant, roads, rail or public amenities. The towers should be oriented cross-wise to the prevailing or any troublesome winds to minimise re-cycling of air from the discharge of one tower to the suction of an adjacent tower. The arrangement of multiple natural draught cooling tower installations should take account of resonant frequencies generated by through-wind velocities.

Consideration should be given to avoiding the possible entrainment of corrosive vapour from adjacent plants and due note should be taken of the position of boiler and other chimneys and flare stacks. Care should be taken in siting buildings adjacent to the air intake of natural draught cooling towers.

The suitability of the ground for the provision of basins needs to be considered.

The relative merits of centralising or decentralising cooling towers or encouraging the use of air coolers should be viewed in the light of future expansion.

1.3.3 Pump and Switch Houses, etc.

As well as placing sub-stations, transformers, switch houses, pumping stations, etc., in places not affected by fire and flood they should also be put in areas which permit non-flameproof equipment to be used unless they form an integral part of a plant.

1.3.4 Distribution of Services

Steam and water mains, electricity and telephone cables, etc., should in general run parallel to the road system and should avoid going through plant areas. It is necessary to make sufficient allowance for pipe and cable tracks so that they do not have to encroach onto roadways or paved areas, either immediately or in future expansions. Typically runs should be initially oversized by about 30% unless a more precise figure can be obtained from predictions about future expansion. The usual clearances between pipes including flanges and lagging, and between pipes and other objects should be 25mm but this should be increased if hot pipes run near plastic pipes, cables, etc.

To prevent freezing, water mains should be buried. Electric power, telephone cables, etc should be run in sand filled trenches. It must be remembered that anchors, bends, valve and motor chambers, cable draw boxes, etc. take up extra space.

Open pipe trenches may be used in places where there is no risk of flammable vapours collecting or of the material freezing, e.g. for steam mains. The minimum width should be 600mm with adequate room left for drainage gullies, trenching machines etc. It is cheaper to have pipes at ground level on sleepers but this method should only be used where access by both vehicles and pedestrians is not hindered. At road

crossings therefore pipes should either drop below ground or be sufficiently raised.

Elevation to the underside of pipe bridges and racks over paved
areas should be at least 3m but preferably 4m and sometimes 7m where
crane access is required. The advantage of these structures is that
pipes can be arranged in double tiers thus reducing overall width.
More details on pipe racks are given in Part II.

References   See References 11–14 on Electrical Distribution.

1.4 Effluent

Liquid effluent can either be storm, plant or soil effluent. In considering the layout of the drainage systems and the effluent plant, early
consultation with the local authorities and consideration of pending
future legislation is advised in order to provide the correct treatment
of all types. Storm water and harmless aqueous plant effluent can be
run in open trenches or sewers but obnoxious aqueous effluents must
be in an enclosed sewer.

Effluent ways should run parallel to the road system. Sewers can be
under the roadway but if possible should be alongside the road so that
any disruption in the sewer is less likely to close the road. Sewers
should have a gradient and be self cleaning. They should be inter-
connected by means of sewer boxes, each of which has a liquid seal to
prevent transmission of gases from one sewer box to another, and the
spread of explosions or fire hazards. In cases where noxious gases
could collect sewer box lids should be closed and sealed, and vented to
a safe location, e.g. 3m above grade, horizontally 4.5m from platforms
and 12m from furnace walls.

The various parts of the site should be graded so that storm water
goes to the appropriate drain. The minimum slope for paved areas in
use is 1 in 80 but for corrosive liquors 1 in 40 is advisable though the
maximum fall in any one direction must not exceed 150mm.

Storm drainage from undeveloped areas and from buildings etc
having no spillable liquids can go direct to the community sewer. Rain
water from areas that are only occasionally contaminated is first
checked in holding ponds before discharge to the sewer. Rain from
frequently contaminated parts should be treated along with the aqueous process effluent. It is essential that these areas are distinct from
each other and from neighbouring property so that cross contamination does not occur. To achieve this, advantage should be taken of
the natural grade in siting the draining systems and the effluent treat-

ment plants. For good community relations an effluent plant should not be sited adjacent to residential or similar property. The actual layout of liquid effluent plant is undertaken just as though it were a process plant. See Part I Section 2.

Incinerators for combustible solids and non aqueous liquids should where practicable be sited convenient to the process supplying the effluent. Solids for dumping should be loaded directly from process to transport. If intermediate storage on site cannot be avoided it should be situated so as to avoid nuisance to the public and other plants in the way of dust, smell, fire risk, seepage, etc.

Gaseous effluent should be burnt or discharged at such a height that in no circumstances can offensive fumes become a public nuisance. The local Alkali Inspector should be consulted with regard to stack heights for gaseous effluent discharge. The effect of any troublesome or prevailing wind should be taken into account.

Reference   See Reference 10 on Effluent.

1.5 Central Buildings

The Appendix to Part I gives typical clearances for central buildings.

1.5.1 Administration Buildings

Administration buildings should be located on the public or safe side of the security point and close to the main entrance if possible. They should be upwind of any plant capable of venting fumes to the atmosphere as should all buildings. Adequate car parking facilities should be provided. The main office building should always be near the main entrance.

1.5.2 Canteens and Medical Centres

Canteens, personnel shops and medical centres should be located in a safe area, preferably with attractive surroundings, and within a short distance of the main concentration of labour. Off loading of food supplies should not interfere with other traffic.

1.5.3 Workshops, General Stores, Garages, etc.

Workshops and general stores (i.e. not process materials) etc. should be located together in a safe area and preferably within easy access of the process units. Direct access should be provided for traffic, which if possible should not pass through process areas. Off loading of stores should not interfere with other traffic. Workshops may need adjacent external space for outside fabrication.

1.5.4 Works Laboratories

Works Laboratories should be central to the plants they serve but in a safe area. If the works laboratories are concerned mainly with effluent and with fuel supplies they can be located near the effluent or steam raising plants.

1.6 Access

Typical road and rail dimensions are given in the Appendix to Part I. Road tanker turning circles are given in *Tables 4* and *5*.

1.6.1 Roads and Parking Areas

In laying out the road system it is necessary to analyse both the immediate and future traffic requirements.

Wherever possible, roads should be arranged so that vehicles do not pass through process areas or violate danger area classifications in reaching their destinations. Roads through plant areas should therefore be laid out only for access to the plant. Ideally the outside of a plant area should be accessible on all four sides by road. Adequate access must be provided to areas where it is known that equipment or material must be brought in for maintenance purposes, e.g. compressor house. Similar access is needed for reactors or converters where it is known that catalyst removal and replacement must be effected. These roads should be wide enough to permit easy manoevring of vehicles and mobile cranes. The entry of handling equipment into the plants from roads should not be obstructed by curbstones, drainage ditches, pipeways at ground level, etc. Access for fire fighting equipment is to be considered. Care should be taken to ensure adequate turning space for tankers and vehicles.

Dual direction roads should allow the passage of two vehicles. Corner radii should suit the turning circle of the largest vehicles and any special loads. Railway crossings, cross roads, road junctions, dead ends, right angle bends and ramps should be as few as possible. Pedestrian pathways adjacent to roads should be allowed for in areas of high personnel concentration and traffic movement. In the sizing of roads, room must be allowed for adjacent drainage channels, especially if the site is low or near surface water.

There should be adequate parking space for vehicles waiting to load or unload, for the weighbridge or to receive clearance to enter or leave the site. Car and bus parks for personnel and visitors and their access roads should be in a safe area and outside security points. The parking area for night-shift employees should be under observation of the gatekeeper.

1.6.2 Rail tracks

Rail tracks within works and rail links with the national system should be laid out in consultation with the local railway authorities to meet the works' requirements for raw material reception and product dispatch. The rail layout should be considered very early on in the layout of a site in conjunction with the road plan as it can have an important effect on, for example, whether whole trains go to one plant on a 'merry-go-round' system or whether trains have to be shunted for breaking and making up in sidings. Account should be taken of any limitations imposed by danger area requirements and any special requirements for rail tanker loading and unloading, with adequate radii at curves for the longest tanker or railcar. Sufficient area should be allowed for drainage of roadbed and for points.

Rail tracks can be an obstruction to operation and maintenace so spurs and rail/road crossings should be kept to a minimum and rail tracks must never cross the main entrance road. Plants needing rail transport should be placed near the railway and those that do not, away from it. A plant should not be boxed in by branch lines.

1.7 Emergency Services

In considering the overall site layout, thought should be given to what will happen in an emergency. Where space permits, a distance of at least 15m, preferably 30m, should separate normal plants so that fire does not spread from the original source. On more dangerous plants this distance should be fixed only after seeking further advice. Failing this, safe distance protective walls are required between plants. The road system should be checked so that no area is likely to be cut off due to an emergency.

The fire and ambulance station should be so located that it will not be affected by a major fire and so that it has good access to all parts of the factory to enable emergency action without hazard to factory traffic.

During the early stages of layout it is useful to speak to the local

Fire Authority about the layout in general but particularly about the layout of the water mains and the positions of hydrants and hose reel points. In general buried water pipes servicing fire hydrants should be laid as ring mains, located alongside the roads adjacent to plants. Sometimes it is useful to take water from natural sources and access to the take off points must be planned.

It is desirable to have a disaster control point and a number of other points about the site containing emergency equipment and connected to it by telephone. In considering the layout for emergency services the effects of, and on, the activities on neighbouring sites should not be forgotten.

Reference   See Reference 55 on Safe Distances.

1.8 Environmental Aspects

The situation of the site can affect layout whilst good layout can minimise detrimental effects on the environment.

Some of the consequences of the choice of a particular site are as follows. Administration buildings should be near the public road, storage areas should be near the rail or water ways, heavier buildings should be on the better load-bearing areas of the site and the topography may be used for gravity flow. Advantage may also be taken of existing contours so that intelligent positioning (making use of computers if need be) of equipment will reduce the amount of earth movement in cutting and filling.

In laying out a site consideration should be made in using the undulations and trees to screen buildings as much as possible. Administration buildings, laboratories etc., but not process plants, can be erected adjacent to residential or similar property. These should have landscaped surroundings to improve appearance. Such buildings can act as noise screens to protect local residents. Processes should not be put next to a neighbour's hazardous operation. In the positioning of plants and buildings early consultation with the local authority is advisable. Also check whether high stacks may cause an aerial hazard and whether warning lights are needed.

Reduction of the effects of effluent can be made by good layout. The prevailing wind direction should be considered so that plants producing gasseous effluents or noise are not up wind of residential property. Liquid effluent must not be allowed to run off plants onto adjacent property, or vice versa. Solid effluents, if they have to be kept on site in heaps prior to transportation, should be remote from adjacent property. Similarly the outside stores of drums or of unwanted or scrap equipment should be out of sight of the boundary. Rail spurs should be placed so that the noise of shunting is minimised. Pollution in all its aspects is causing increasing concern and pressures, legislation, etc., will have a marked effect in the future on the layout of chemical plants.

Factory gates should be sited so that the affect of personnel coming off duty on the outside traffic is small. Lorries should not have to pass through residential areas to reach the works and not have to queue on the public road to gain entrance to the site.

1.9 Geographical Factors

It must be stressed that, in this book, it is implicitly assumed that the plant is being constructed in the United Kingdom. In cases where the plant is being constructed elsewhere it is vital that the following geographic factors be taken into account.

The direction of the prevailing wind differs in different parts of the world and this affects the position of, say, cooling towers which have to be to the leeside of the plant.

Of prime importance is to remember that, south of the equator, the sun is in the *north* at noon. In hot and sunny climates some items, such as refrigerated store tanks, may have to be sited in the shade and this demands a knowledge of the direction and elevation of the sun. In some countries frost protection for pipes, buried or unburied, is totally unnecessary. In others far more stringent protection is required. It should be remembered that as temperatures fall more, more liquids become liable to freeze.

Rainfall may vary from practically nil to heavy monsoon conditions (up to 10cms per hour) and this obviously has a very great effect upon the provision of surface water drainage. Care should be taken in layout to avoid the flooding of sensitive areas such as pump pits and bunded areas which may, if flooded, cause the tanks in them to float.

In certain parts of the world severe thunderstorms occur as frequently as one day in three. In such climates all equipment must be laid out to lie within a 120° cone of a lightning conductor. Great care has to be exercised in laying out plant in earthquake susceptible areas and local advice must be sought.

In some countries open fire box railway engines are still used. In these cases hazardous areas must not overlap the tracks.

All these factors may affect whether buildings are enclosed or open structured see Part I Section 2.2.1.

2 PLANT LAYOUT

2.1 General

Given a flow sheet and an area of land the possible layout arrangements are unlimited but it cannot be too strongly emphasised that the considerations underlying the layout of a chemical plant are often the most important factors in the effective, safe and economic realisation of the process.

The theoretical minimum space a plant can occupy is the total volume of its various components. Various constraints prevent the attainment of this minimum. Such constraints include allowing adequate clearances for access during operation, maintenance and construction and to allow safe operation.

In general it is true to say that the most economical plant layout is that in which the spacing of the main equipment items is such that it minimises interconnecting pipework and structural steel work. Normally, equipment should be laid out in a sequence to suit the process flow but exceptions to this arise from the desirability to group certain items such as tanks or pumps or perhaps to isolate hazardous operations. The use of single stream or multiple stream flow patterns will affect layout as will the need to duplicate all or some of the functional stages.

Whilst many of the variables affecting the final layout are readily quantified and such aspects as pipe sizing, insulation thickness, steelwork spacing may be optimised by well known techniques, matters of operational convenience, safety, ease of erection and maintenance call for the exercise of critical judgement based on experience and the study of existing plants and their known limitations.

2.1.1 Economic Considerations

Equipment should be laid out to give the maximum economy of pipework and supporting steel. As a general rule, as compact a layout as possible with all equipment at ground level is the first objective consistent with access and safety requirements.

The cost of positioning equipment in structures of more than two floors is inflated by the need to provide access platforms and stairways whilst the compensations from saving ground space and enclosure costs become less important. Above 30m the cost of operator safety becomes increasingly heavy. In general, high elevation should be only considered when ground space is limited or where gravity flow of materials is essential or desirable. Note that moderate elevation is needed

15

to provide pump suction head requirements or a driving head around a thermosyphon reboiler. Exchangers may be elevated but in the absence of a process consideration this should only be carried out if economies in pipework and floor space balance the cost of elevation. Equipement should be located to minimise extensive pipe runs as these increase costs by reason of the additional pipe used, the extra insulation needed, greater heat losses, more devices to accommodate expansion and by greater pumping costs.

Considerations should be given to optimising the use of supporting structures in concrete or steel by duplicating their application to more than one item of equipment and ensuring that accessways, platforms, etc. have more than one function. Space saving can be achieved by locating small equipment such as pumps under the pipe bridge or rack, providing this area is not needed for access.

Small vessels, air-fin exchangers and similar equipment may be located over the main pipeways provided the additional expense of the increased steel sections with possible additional access platforms and heavier foundations to the bridge or rack can justify the saving in ground space, and that it does not increase construction difficulties or delays.

Removal of heat exchanger tube bundles or internals from process vessels may influence the positioning of equipment above ground level and the effect of this on the cost of supporting structure and extended process and utilities pipework must be evaluated.

2.1.2 Safety Considerations

Where toxic or otherwise hazardous materials are handled, layout may be complicated by the need to isolate sections of the plant. Equipment items which could be considered a possible source of hazard should be grouped together and where possible located separately from other areas of the plant. Examples of this are furnaces, flare stacks or other equipment containing naked flames; rotating or mechanical equipment handling flammable or volatile liquids which could easily leak or spill out of the equipment thus causing a flammable centre. However such considerations should not override considerations of cost, for instance process heaters must necessarily be located close to other equipment to conserve expensive alloy piping. Furnaces using gas as a feedstock do not normally constitute a hazard.

Equipment handling acids or other toxic materials which could cause damage or endanger personnel by their spillage, should, in general, be grouped together. If fluids from two different leaking tanks can react together in an undesirable way, then kerbs should be placed to prevent intermixing. Ventilation requirements should be considered at an early stage as well as types of flooring since open flooring lets through fumes.

To isolate hazardous areas it may be necessary to build walls with self-closing doors or even with connecting rooms fitted with showers, where clothing has to be changed.

Definitions of hazardous areas are given in BS CP 1003 (see *Reference 56*) and in the Institute of Petroleum Codes (see *Reference 59*).

In addition to the requirements of these Safety Codes, a check should be made with the local bye-laws and the Fire and Alkali Office whose requirements may be more stringent or specific than the above codes or these procedures, and should in all such cases take precedence.

Hazardous areas should be located so that they do not overlap the plot limits or the railways. If they do overlap then an unnecessary restriction may be placed on these adjacent areas. In addition hazardous areas should contain only the hazardous operations in order to reduce the need for special equipment such as flameproof motors or extra ventilation.

Considerations should be taken in the equipment layout for the provision of sufficient clear area between critical and mechanically dangerous or high temperature items of equipment to allow for the safety of operating or maintenance personnel. (It is sometimes necessary to insulate pipes for operators' protection and machine guards may be adequate for operators but not high enough for maintenance men.) The layout of lifts, hoists, etc., should be made with operator and maintenance safety in mind (see *Reference 58*). Adequate lighting should be provided.

Clear routes for the operators should be allowed avoiding curbs and other awkward level changes and providing two or more escape exits from platforms and gangways. Safe routes must be planned for fork lift trucks and clear routes must be provided for access by fire-fighting equipment. The layout of isolating switches, local alarms, safety notices, etc., needs consideration. Further details on staircases and guard rails are given in Part I Section 2.2 on buildings.

The Safety Officer should be consulted before the final layout is approved.

References   See References 56–66 on Safety.

2.1.3 Process Considerations

Process considerations may suggest that some items be elevated to provide gravity flow of materials, to accommodate pump suction requirements, provide drawing head around a thermosyphon reboiler, or to allow the use of barometric condensers. Other process considerations could be limitations of pressure or temperature drop in transfer lines deciding the proximity of furnaces, reactors, and columns. The isolation of hazardous areas was discussed in Part I Section 2.1.2.

2.1.4 Operational Considerations

Thought should be given to the location of equipment requiring frequent attendance by operating personnel and the relative position of the control room to obtain the shortest and most direct routes for operators when on routine operation. However, the control room should be in a safe area. In extreme cases, plant manning may be affected by the inability of one operator to attend widely spaced operational controls. Valves should be placed so that they are easily accessible and indicators placed at a height so that they are easily readable. These points are discussed further in Part II Section 3. Generally a batch or semi-batch process needs more attention by the operator and therefore more consideration has to be paid to the ergonomics of the layout. This can be seen in Part II in the sections dealing with batch reactors, batch dryers, plate and frame presses and packaging lines. Even in continuous plants it helps to locate starters so that the operator can see or hear the pump, mixer, etc., start up or shut down as he operates the switch. See section on pumps in Part II. Safety considerations as they affect layout have already been discussed in Part I Section 2.1.2.

2.1.5 Maintenance Considerations

The need to remove for servicing, re-tubing or replacement, heavy and indivisible plant units will dictate their location when access for cranes is needed. The use of rotating or other machinery calling for regular dismantling often makes their grouping within a machine house desirable. The positioning of items needing replacement of internals, spent catalyst, etc., or frequent internal cleaning has to be carefully considered. Valves and instruments should be laid out for ease of operation and maintenance.

2.1.6 Constructional Considerations

The plot should be so designed that adequate access is available to lift large items of equipment or columns into place (see *Figure 3*). When such equipment is positioned close to boundary limits so that

Figure 3 *Construction access (by courtesy of Woodhall Duckham Ltd.)*

erection must take place from outside these limits, a careful check must be undertaken to ascertain whether space will be available at the time of the erection for positioning cranes or lifting tackle. Consideration should also be given to long delivery items of equipment which it is known may well arrive fairly late in the construction programme and therefore have to be fitted into place after most of the surrounding equipment has already been installed.

It is important that the insulation requirements be considered during the layout of plant. Insulation decreases the available free space for access, affects the sizing of tank supports, valve spindles, etc., and alters the siting of pipework, instruments or electrical equipment. Space is also needed for installing the lagging itself. In particular, the thickness of insulation of very high temperature or low temperature piping may be considerable, thus effectively increasing the o/d of the pipe. Additional clearance must be provided around control valves, instrumentation etc., to allow for the additional thickness of insulation.

2.1.7 Appearance

As a rule an attractively laid out plant with equipment in rows is also an economically laid out plant.

Preference should be given to having a single pipeway with a minimum number of side branches. This pipeway may be in the form of ring main as this can obviate a complete shut down for repairing leakages, etc. Buildings, structures and groups of equipment should form a neat, symmetrical balanced layout, consistent with keeping pipe runs to a minimum, and allowing proper access for maintenance. Towers and large vertical vessels should be arranged in rows with a common centre line if of similar size but if the diameters vary they should be lined up with a common face. Due note must be taken of building lines. Manholes on adjacent towers should be at a similar elevation and orientation to present uniformity of platforms and of appearances generally.

The centre lines of exchanger channel nozzles should be lined up, as should the centre lines of pump discharge nozzles. Piping around pumps, exchangers and similar ground level equipment should be run wherever possible at a set elevation for north to south piping and another elevation for east to west piping. These elevations being to 'bottom of pipe' or underside of shoe for insulated lines. This should also help to achieve a common elevation for off-takes from pipeways.

Where there are duplicated streams these, as far as possible, should be made identical. Such arrangements for parallel streams or similar groups of process equipment have many advantages not only in the economies gained in the design work but also for construction and subsequently operation and in reducing the amount of standby equipment. In particular handed arrangements should be avoided. This principle may also be followed where there are similar equipment sequences within the process stream, i.e. fractionating column with its overhead condensers, reflux drum pumps and re-boiler, etc., is an example of a system which could be repeated in an almost identical way.

2.1.8 Future Expansion

Thought should be given to likely future expansion of both equipment and pipework so that the additions can be erected and tested with the minimum interference to plant operation. On main pipe runs it is desirable to leave 30% spare space. At least 30m distance from a flameproof plant area is needed for safe welding where no special precautions are taken. On the other hand the probable positioning of additions should not involve excessive runs of pipework to link up with the existing plant. The distance is fixed by balancing the cost of extra piping against the cost of taking precautions during erection including the possibility of shutting down and purging out.

2.2 Buildings

2.2.1 Choice of Building

Plant buildings should be kept to a minimum on the basis that most items of equipment including pumps, heat exchangers, boilers, cyclones etc., may be safely installed in the open. The philosophy should be that plant is supported on open steel structures unless there is a good reason to do otherwise. Thus most automated or continous plants tend to be in the open with centralised control facilities housed in buildings.

Factors which determine the selection of partially clad structures or enclosed building are:

1) **Nature and frequency of operator's work.**
   Equipment that requires frequent (greater than weekly) maintenance in adverse weather conditions should be placed in an enclosed building. Partially clad open structures may be used.

2) **Climate.**
   Extreme climatic conditions may determine that a plant be in a building. This will increase operating efficiency. However when lack of shelter only causes transitory inconvenience, outdoor plant should be considered.

3) **Type of equipment.**
   Expensive equipment and complex machinery should have some degree of weatherproofing. Electrical switchgear and control equipment should also be enclosed, and in accordance with Statutory Regulations (see *Reference 19*).

4) **Nature of process.**
   Plants handling, dusty, explosive and combustible solid materials require a building. To prevent contamination, food, pharmaceutical and some other biochemical plants also require to be in a building.

5) **Proximity of hazards.**
To prevent the possible spread of fire and explosion when the spacing of hazardous process units is restricted, a building may be desirable. However, from a general hazard point of view, it is preferable to restrict the use of buildings and consider using protective walls.

6) **Noise factor.**
Reciprocating gas compressors, steam/gas turbines, diesel engines, etc., may be in a building to enclose the noise source. The building should be internally clad with sound absorptive materials.

It is fundamental that the buildings should be built around the process instead of the process being made to fit buildings of conventional design.

Plant offices, laboratories, maintenance, first aid points and amenities, facilities (mess room, changing rooms, lavatories) should, if practicable, be grouped in safe areas adjacent to large process plants or groups of process plants.

Process buildings and structures should be located adjacent to a road or access-way to allow for servicing and access of fire appliances.

The distance between buildings or structures should be equal to half the height, or higher side if unequal, or 9m whichever is the greater. Buildings or structures handling dusty, explosive or combustible material should be located a minimum of 15m from hot process equipment, electrical switch-gear and similar hazards.

2.2.2 Open Structures

When plant items require to be supported at elevated levels (defined as 3.5m above grade for vessels, 2m above grade for instruments, or 2m above another platform) to suit the process layout, platforms must be provided for operation and maintenance. These are reached by stairways, ladders or lifts. The number of intermediate floor levels should be kept to a minimum. This is helped by an intelligent arrangement of manholes, operating valves, instruments, maintenance and inspection points. When, after consideration of economics and process factors, gravity flow from point to point is advantageous, multi-storey or at least a tall single storey structure is provided, in order that the equipment may be supported at its correct level.

Floors are generally not less than 3m apart. Minimum headroom under pipes, cable racks etc., should be not less than 2.25m. This figure can be reduced to 2.1m vertically over stairways. In establishing distances between floors it is important to allow for the removal of agitator shafts and other vessel internals.

For main access, stairways are preferred to ladders, the latter being used for emergency escape routes and to isolated positions where attention is infrequently required. Multi-storey structures less than 8m in length must be provided with at least one stairway. Those over 8m with at least two stairways. In all cases fire escape ladders must be provided to prevent operators being trapped. Exits should be arranged so that no point on an operating platform shall be more than 30m from an exit, and the length of dead end platforms is not greater than 8m. The approval of the local Fire Authority should be sought regarding the adequacy of means of escape from multi-floor structures.

Recommended angle for steel stairways is 35°–40° and an overall width of 1m should be allowed for layout purposes. Maximum height of single flights without intermediate landing is 4.5m. Ladders may be vertical, or inclined at an angle up to 15° with a plan of 1m squared allowed in the layout (see *Figure 4*). They should be arranged for side exit though step through ladders may be used for runs from grade up to 10m or for elevated runs of 3m. Maximum ladder height without landing is 10m. Back cages or safety hoops must be provided for ladders over 2.5m high. Intermediate steps are needed for elevation changes in excess of 380mm. Further details on stairs, ladders, can be found in EEUA Handbook No. 7 (see *Reference 20*).

General access ways should not be less than 1m wide but special consideration must be given to access around plant items. At maintenance points, where maybe internals have to be removed, a sufficiently wide solid platform should be provided.

Lifting beams and davits must be provided where necessary for maintenance purposes.

2.2.3 Enclosed Buildings

All notes in section 2.2.2 apply equally to enclosed buildings.

If the choice is for an enclosed building, the selection of building type should be made early. Generally the internal structure is steel. For processes such as biochemical that are carried out in 'clean' conditions, concrete and ceramics are used as they can be shaped to give non-dust collecting and easily cleaned surfaces. Consideration must then be given to the following factors:

1) **Fire Protection.**

Approval by the local Fire Authority must be obtained on the layout of fire fighting equipment. An automatic sprinkler system may be employed. Attention should be given to the location of fire buckets and extinguishers at strategic points. The fire hydrants should be intelligently located, the hose being reeled or hung at a convenient height, permanently attached to a pipe line.

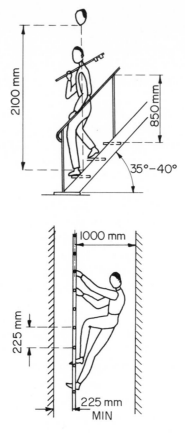

Figure 4   *Stair and fixed ladder layout*

2) Illumination.

Natural illumination may be obtained by use of patent glazing, windows, or translucent sheets in the side walls, or the roof. Roof lights may also be individual sky-lights. *North light* roof construction gives a good uniform natural light without the disadvantages of direct sunlight glare. Artificial lighting must be arranged to give adequate illumination throughout and extra light points near equipment where physical and chemical hazards exist, and where instruments are read.

3) Flameproofing.

It will be necessary to determine early if a plant is to be flame proof. This could affect plant arrangement and position of switchroom.

4) Ventilation.

There should be a careful study of ventilation requirements for each installation. Air intakes should be positioned remote from adjoining process plants to avoid the risk of drawing in toxic or hazardous fumes. Exhaust air may require treatment by separation, washing or filtering etc. Intake and exhaust ducts should be so placed to avoid short circuiting.

5) **Heating.**

Process requirement and operational working conditions must be considered. The type of heating system should be known in the layout stage in order that room is left for the equipment.

6) **Access.**

In enclosed buildings thought should be given to providing a door of sufficient size to permit passage of the largest single section of equipment contained in the building. In multi-storey plants, holes are required in floors to accommodate the largest vessel cover. Ideally these wells should be guarded with hand-railing, and provided with lifting beams above. The position of a goods hoist should be considered, and if required, positioned intelligently, to avoid unnecessary handling across floors.

7) **Roofing.**

Flat roofs can be used to store (harmless only) liquids in tanks and other vessels on or above the roof. Pitched roofs enable snow and water to clear quicker, and makes the installation of roof lighting and ventilation easier.

2.2.4 Control Room Layout

The control room siting and construction should be such that explosion or fire in the process area cannot in itself put the control room out of action. For economic reasons the control room buildings should preferably be located in a safe area and not in a hazardous area as defined in BS CP 1003 (see *Reference 17*). Also the building should be so sited that a minimum of vibration is transmitted to the structure of the room. Windows should give operators any necessary view of the process area, subject to protection from fire, etc., mentioned above. They should face north if possible since this avoids direct sunlight onto instruments and annunciators which can result in lights not being visible on a panel face.

Direct access should be provided from the control room to the plant and if possible to rooms provided for computers, data loggers and associated equipment for instrumentation but so arranged that the control room will not become a thoroughfare. The building containing the control room may include ancillary rooms such as locker rooms, mess room, toilet facilities, offices for supervisors and clerical personnel, test room (laboratory tests), instrument servicing

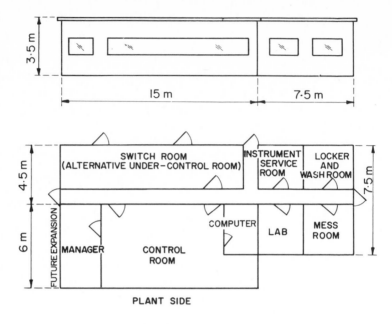

Figure 5   *Control building layout*

room, electric relay and switch rooms, (see *Figure 5*). In some cases cabling may be reduced by putting the switch room in a basement under the control room. Apart from this it is advisable to have all rooms at ground level.

Provision for the possible extension of the control room should be considered. An adjacent area of plot plan should be reserved and structural features such as internal cable trenches arranged as to connect to the extension.

Figure 6   *Typical control panel layout (by courtesy of ICI Ltd.)*

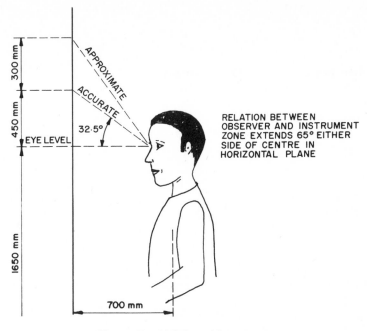

Figure 7 *Heights of instruments*

The instruments needed for the area of control exercised by any one process operator should be grouped together. A clear demarcation should be made on the panel between process units. Instruments should be arranged so that the variables requiring the most critical attention are in a position of optimum visibility and manual accessibility. Related variables should be displayed adjacent to each other (see *Figure 6*). As a secondary criterion, instruments should occupy relative positions according to the sequence and situation of process items (see *Reference 18*).

In general the height from the floor to the top of the highest control or recording instrument should be no greater than 2.1m and the top of the lowest instrument not less than 1.2m (see *Figure 7*). Panel space between 2.1m and 2.4m may be used for pressure indicators, visual alarm systems and similar instruments. For free-standing, or U-type panels, the space behind the panel must give an unobstructed passage of 1m. In front of the panel 3m should be allocated, leading to an overall width of control room of 16m allowing for panel width. The length is determined by the number of instruments.

References See References 17–20 on Enclosed Buildings and Control Room Layout

3 TECHNIQUES FOR LAYOUT

3.1 The Principles of Layout Development

There is no single technique leading to the best arrangement in any problem; several stages may be required, with different techniques appropriate to each.

The development process is repeated at successive stages. Thus, according to the problem, layout may be considered at several levels from the selection of a site and arrangement of the plants on it, through block layout relating plant sections to one another, to the detailed planning of working areas and the equipment in them.

To this approach one may relate the three basic principles of layout planning:

1) **Plan the whole, then the detail.**
Individual aspects must be subservient to the whole, and sub-optimisation avoided.
2) **Plan the ideal, and from it the practical.**
The ideal is free from restrictions and gives a datum, the cost of departing from which can be set against the advantages to be gained.
3) **Plan more than one layout.**
It is seldom that a single layout is 'best' for each criterion. Planning more than one permits comparisons and leads to greater confidence in making the final selection.

3.1.1 Sequence of Activities in Layout

A simplified network showing the integration of plant layout and design activities is given in *Figure 8*. (See *Reference 41*). The network can be subdivided into various stages in the development of the layout. These are illustrated in *Table 1* for the location of plant items relative to each other. The various techniques are discussed in detail in Part I Section 3.2.

After this stage engineering detail is examined, e.g., location of controls, instruments, piping. It may be that the additional information now available will modify some of the earlier constraints. This may involve re-examination of earlier alternatives previously rejected.

Reference　See References 40 and 41 on Layout Techniques.

3.2 Details of Techniques for Layout

3.2.1 Initial Development of the Layout

For many plants in the chemical industry, layout is by process flow (assemble in sequence of operations and materials moved). The initial development of the layout is carried out using flow sheets supplemented where necessary by process outline, multiple activity charts, etc. Alternatives which are used to a greater extent in light engineering include (see *Reference 43*) layout by fixed position (all operations performed with materials in one fixed location) and layout by process function (similar operations located together).

The initial development of the layout for many plants is possible using layout analogues, such as block models, cut outs, etc. For complex situations these have physical limitations and should be used either following or in conjunction with other techniques which attempt to produce an early assessment of the problem. Such an approach attempts to establish the objectives, to record the limitations and restrictions, to examine their validity, and to check their consistency. The critical examination stage of method study can be used for this purpose (see *Reference 42*). For a full examination of the process the full technique is used and questions are asked as indicated in *Table 2*. However by the layout stage interest is focussed on 'place' (i.e. where it is to go). This is then questioned with 'why is it to go there?' and finally preferred alternatives 'where else could it go?' are explored. When this has all been done, the next step is to apply them to the problem, to determine what arrangements or groups of arrangements are ruled out and which remain as possibilities; and of these to select for further development any that may compare favourably with the others.

An example of critical examination might be:

1) **Where is the plant item placed?**
     The overhead condenser is above the column.
2) **Why is it placed there?**
     Convenient for gravity flow of reflux.
3) **Where else could it go?**
     Near ground level with a pumped reflux.

Techniques of Correlation and Compatibility can be used formally in eliminating what is impossible or inadmissible. Also they can be used in listing, for evaluation, arrangements compatible with the objectives and constraints as stated, in cases where it is not practicable to do this mentally. The list of possible arrangements obtained in this way will usually need further reduction before it becomes practicable to begin detailed evaluation. The selection might be made on qualitative criteria, by a semi quantitative method using critical examination (see *Table 3*) or by determining the controlling costs and proceeding to minimise them. Controlling costs are those that vary most significantly from one feasible layout to another.

To determine controlling costs the linkages between all the items are recorded and a cost per distance run obtained for each.

For example, between:

1) **Buildings.**
Pipes; material transfers; sizes of surrounds for access, aesthetics, extension or development.
2) **Plant items.**
Pipes; conveyors; man movements.
3) **Components.**
Connections; access for fitting, maintenance.
4) **Materials.**
Supply and delivery points; quantities and rates of movement; stores.

It is then possible to determine which of such costs are of major importance in comparing different arrangements. Further details of these techniques are given in Part I Section 3.2.2.

3.2.2 Techniques of Correlation and Compatibility

The Correlation Chart   The Correlation Chart is a diagrammatic method of determining the effect of constraints and recording the arrangements that they allow. In some cases objectives or preferences can also be applied as constraints so narrowing the field still further.

A grid is drawn with the rows representing possible positions—such as floor in a building, or numbered positions in an area—of one plant item, and the columns representing possible positions of another plant item. Constraints are recorded and labelled, say, X, Y, Z ... ; When any constraint prohibits an item going into a particular position then the appropriate square is struck out by writing in it the reference label of that constraint. Vacant squares thus show permitted combinations.

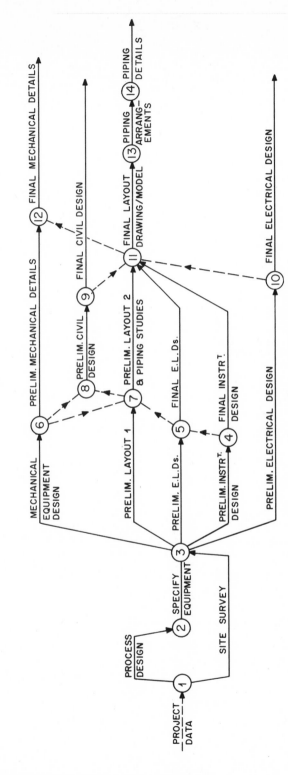

Figure 8 *Typical plant layout and design network*

Table 1 *Typical stages in plant layout*

Stage in the Development of the Layout	Useful Technique
1) Layout begins with the collection and assessment of flowsheets (which must show materials of construction, size of pipework and suggested elevations), equipment data sheets, results of site survey (incorporating relevant data on site boundaries, topography, soil structure, weather conditions, utility terminals and site access points (see *References 40*) and codes of practice.	**Critical examination** is used to question the elevation layout assumptions made in the flowsheet. This method enables the objectives and constraints to be defined. **Techniques of correlation and compatibility** are used to sort and list the various alternatives.
2) The cost of each elevation alternative is examined for differences only, e.g. in the number of plant items needed to achieve the objective; in the material transfer costs such as piping, elevators, power consumption.	**Simple elevation drawings** are prepared for the alternatives showing heights and relative positions of plant items only. No structure or floor levels are added yet as these may depend on plan layout.
3) Plant items and buildings are laid out in plan, ensuring that all layout constraints (e.g. relating to operation, maintenance, safety construction, environments and expansion) are applied. A costing is made of each plan layout similar to the elevation study.	**Critical examination** is used to question the plan layout assumptions made in the flowsheet. Once the constraints are defined **Techniques of correlation and compatibility** are again used to sort and list the various alternatives. **Layout analogues** such as cut outs help in the visualisation of the layout and in the examination of plot size and external constraints.

4) The selected plan and elevation layouts are now combined to determine possible positions of supporting and access structures, and to study civil requirements. These may force relaxation of earlier constraints.	The layout alternatives are presented by **block models**. At this stage these help people to visualise the non-quantifiable operational and safety aspects.
5) Final alternatives are again costed for differences and a selection is made.	The final layout is **drawn** (options may still be left open for detailed study).
6) Preparation of piping models is now commenced. These are further used to optimise pipework. A check should be made that all constraints are obeyed particularly those for operation.	**Piping models** are now prepared.

Table 2 *Critical examination sheet*

The Present Facts		Alternatives	Selection for Development
WHAT is achieved?	WHY?	WHAT ELSE could be achieved?	WHAT SHOULD be achieved?
HOW is it achieved?	WHY THAT WAY?	HOW ELSE could it be achieved?	HOW SHOULD it be achieved?
WHEN is it achieved?	WHY THEN?	WHEN ELSE could it be achieved?	WHEN SHOULD it be achieved?
WHERE is it achieved?	WHY THERE	WHERE ELSE could it be achieved?	WHERE SHOULD it be achieved?
WHO achieves it?	WHY THAT PERSON?	WHO ELSE could achieve it?	WHO SHOULD achieve it?

The sets of lines of the grid can be extended and crossed by rows or columns representing other items, and prohibitions or preferences again applied. When all constraints have been applied then squares that remain open represent possible permutations of those two items. Paths are traced along the rows of the grid, from the first item through to the last, connecting only open squares. If any such path connects all items without violating any of the constraints, then it represents a feasible solution of the problem.

The advantages of this method are its visual presentation, and the ease with which it can be learnt and used; the disadvantages are the amount of drawing-up required, and difficulty in correlating items that are not contiguous on the chart.

As an example of this method consider the following process, the outline process chart for which is as in *Figure 9*.

The problem is one of vertical layout and is to arrange the vessels for these process stages on the five floors (Ground, 1st, 2nd, 3rd, 4th) of an existing building.

Conditions apply as follows:

Constraints

1) Reaction Vessel and Pressure Filter discharge from below and should not be put on the Ground Floor.

2) The Pressure Filter is not to go on the 4th floor, as there would not be enough room to withdraw the spindle for maintenance.

3) The Storage Hopper (S) must be above a Weigh Hopper, which is situated on the 1st floor.

Objectives

4) It is desired to leave the Reaction and Acid Treatment Vessels in their present position on the 2nd and 1st floors respectively.

5) For reason of heat transfer and gravity flow, Melting should be adjacent to Reaction and above it.

6) For ease of handling the cake from the Pressure Filter it should be dropped directly into the Drier.

7) Subject to all other conditions, the cost of lifting materials is to be minimised.

Apart from the possibility of some floors becoming over-congested, there is no constraint in this problem on items 'sharing' a position. Constraint *1)* states that neither R nor F must be on the ground floor, and these squares are deleted with a figure 1.

Table 3 *Comparison of plot plans*

Factor	Arrangement A Plot plan drawing No.				Arrangement B Plot plant drawing No.			
	Remarks	Rating	Correl. value	Adjusted rating	Remarks	Rating	Correl. value	Adjusted rating
A. Safety:								
1. Does relative layout of facilities minimise hazard of fire or explosion?			10				10	
2. Is access to various facilities satisfactory for fire fighting or escape?			5				5	
3. Is fire control and extinguishment affected by wind, grades, fire-water system, foam system, dike volumes etc.			10				10	
B. Operation:								
1. Does plot result in low-cost operations as related to following:								
a. Oil transfer			5				5	
b. Utilities			5				5	
c. Product loading			5				5	
d. Waste disposal			5				5	
2. Is convenience of operation and supervision affected by following:								
a. Terraces and grades			5				5	
b. Relative locations of services			5				5	
c. Access by road and rail			5				5	

C. Maintenance:

1. Will layout result in reasonable cost of maintenance of offsite facilities including earthen dikes and other structures, roads and piping?   10   10

2. Is arrangement of equipment, access roadways, and extent of paving convenient for maintenance?   5   5

D. Expansion:

1. Is amount of space for expansion adequate?   2   2

2. Is location of space for expansion in proper relationship with regard to present and future?   1   1

3. Is additional property available?   1   1

4. Can storage and product systems be expanded?   3   3

5. Can utility generating and distribution facilities be expanded?   3   3

E. Construction:

1. Does layout minimise problems related to physical factors such as foundation conditions, ground and surface water, sloping terrain etc.?   3   3

2. Is working and storage space available for present and future?   2   2

continued overleaf

Table 3 (cont.)

F. Initial Cost:		
1. Does layout minimise initial cost of following:		
a. Earth moving, roads and rail-roads	2	2
b. Oil piping	2	2
c. Utility piping	1	1
d. Electrical distribution	1	1
e. Pumps	1	1
2. Is initial cost affected by following:		
a. Need for special structures as retaining walls	1	1
b. Amount of waste space	1	1
c. Re-location of existing facilities	1	1

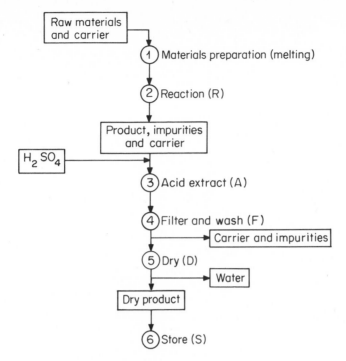

Figure 9 *Progress chart*

Constraint *2)* prevents F from being on floor 4; the squares are deleted with *2)*.

Constraint *3)* means that S must be on floors 2, or 3, or 4; other squares deleted with *3)*.

These result in the grid shown in *Figure 10*; they are the absolute exclusions. The other conditions are objectives and might be relaxed if that proved necessary. The grid is now developed further as in *Figure 11* by applying the objectives as follows:

Objective *4)* limits R to floor 2 and A to floor 1.

Objective *5)* now prevents M from being on the ground, 1st or 2nd floors; it also prefers M_3 to M_4 and this is shown by deleting $M_4 R_2$ with a bracketed number.

Objective *6)* deletes all floors of D that are not below the corresponding floor for F.

Objective *7)* is best applied whilst tracing paths through the grid. The path must begin $M_3 R_2 A_1$.

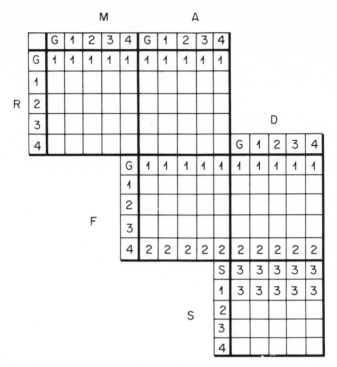

Figure 10   *Grid showing absolute exclusions*

Then $F_1 D_G$
  or $F_2 D_1$, (or $F_2 D_G$ which violates (7))
  or $F_3 D_2$, (or $F_3 D_1$, $F_3 D_G$ which violate (7))
Then to S_2, (or S_3, S_4, which violate (7))
So the three possibilities are:
  M_3 R_2 A_1 F_1 D_G S_2
  M_3 R_2 A_1 F_2 D_1 S_2
and M_3 R_2 A_1 F_3 D_2 S_2

The first of these is shown traced out in *Figure 11*.

Algebraic Method   In this method the possible positions for different items are represented by algebraic symbols; thus A   means item A in position 1. Ordinary rules of algebra can then be used with the special meanings that is,

	addition	represents alternatives
and	multiplication	represents co-existence

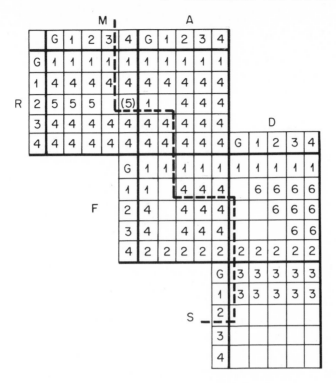

Figure 11   *Grid showing permissible layouts*

Thus A_1 (B_2 + B_3) means item A in position 1, with item B in either position 2 or position 3.

If a permutation is inadmissible it is put equal to zero—i.e. it is deleted. It is not necessary to multiply out brackets when applying constraints, and it may be possible to impose more than one of these at the same time. On multiplying out at any stage, the terms represent all the permutations still allowable at that stage.

This method is not so simple as the Correlation Chart, but is more powerful in dealing with multiple permutations and easier to read, though not to visualise.

Considering the previous problem with the same progress chart (*Figure 9*) and constraints and objectives applicable:

Constraint *1)* means that R_G and F_G are eliminated.

Constraint *2)* means that F_4 is eliminated.

Constraint *3)* means that S_G and S_1 are eliminated.

So all feasible layouts are represented by:

$(M_{G,1\ ..4})\ (R_{1\ ..4})\ (A_{G,1\ ..4})\ (F_{1,2,3})\ (D_{G,1\ ..4})\ (S_{2,3,4})$

Objective 4) implies that R_2 and A_1 are to be chosen if possible.

Objective 5) implies that M_3 or M_4 should be chosen; of these M_3 is nearer to R, and so is to be preferred.

Objective 6) implies $F_1\,D_G + F_2(D_G + D_1) + F_3(D_G + D_1 + D_2)$

To apply Objective 7) first consider what lifting may be necessary:

This is   slurry from A to F

and/or   powder from D to S

Objective 7) then rules out S_3 and S_4 as not minimal; similarly it rules out F_2D_G, F_3D_G, F_3D_1 all of which impose more *lifting* than the other three relations between F and D.

The terms to be evaluated in terms of the costs of moving slurry and powder are then reduced to:

$M_3R_2A_1F_1D_GS_2$: slurry moved horizontally on floor 1; powder to be raised from G to 2.

$M_3R_2A_1F_3D_2S_2$: slurry to be raised from 1 to 3; powder moved horizontally on floor 2.

$M_3R_2A_1F_2D_1S_2$: slurry and powder each raised one floor from 1 to 2.

Note: Should it transpire later that there is congestion on any of the floors then additional lifting costs may be accepted. Terms like M_4 or S_3 could be brought back into consideration.

3.2.3 Proximity and Sequencing.

The Travel Chart   These were originally used for siting machines in jobbing shops, and the name related to the record of the amount of travel of different jobs between the machines.

A square grid is drawn and labelled across and down with the names of each item: every square is the meeting point of a row and a column, each representing an item. In it is inserted the total cost per unit distance of all linkages between these two items. In the case of neighbouring items this cost will lie in a square next to the main diagonal; for items that are not neighbours the cost will lie in a square away from the main diagonal. The total cost of linking all items is found by multiplying the cost in each square by the distance of that square from the main diagonal and summing. Visual inspection of the columns then shows which interchanges (permutations of the items) would reduce this total cost by bringing certain costs nearer the main diagonal. The process is repeated until an optimum arrangement has been reached.

This method can be modified to compensate in part for different plant sizes. As a method of approximating, certain simplifications can be made: for example it can be used with just the significant costs, again, groups of items that are to be sited near to one another can be treated as a single item with 'group' linkages to other items.

The main disadvantage of the method is that it only leads to an optimum linear arrangement, which is seldom wanted; on the other hand it measures the relative importance of having different pairs of items close to one another, which is a useful first step to the two- or three-dimensional problem.

Two and Three Dimensional Proximities Some computational routines have been devised for these, (see Part I Section 3.4) but without the use of a computer they are unwieldy. The simplest manual method is probably one of trial and error in which items are situated near to one another as suggested by significant costs, and the arrangement modified by reference to the travel chart.

Sequencing Techniques Although mainly used to find feasible sequences of operations in a process, sequencing techniques may sometimes be useful in layout problems. They are based on a grid similar to the Travel Chart, but usually simpler; for example, costs may refer only to vertical transports, or costs may be omitted and symbols used to indicate inadmissibility or preference. Instead of permuting the items, however, chain diagrams are prepared (similar to outline process charts), starting from some key item of plant or some key position (e.g. ground level); these are prepared on a basis of 'preferred links', till all items have been included in one chain or another. The next step is to consider simplification by combining items at the same level or in neighbouring positions, and schematic diagrams may be prepared, showing other links such as access, etc. Finally, the most promising chains may be rough costed, or otherwise compared, and the best selected for study in greater detail.

Reference See References 42 and 43 on Layout Techniques.

3.3 Layout Analogues.

3.3.1 Cut Outs.

Cut-outs are made to scale, e.g. 1 : 50 from celluloid or cardboard. These may represent equipment or buildings. Usually the area represents the actual size of the equipment and building. For less experienced 'layout engineers the area may represent the plot area required for the operation of each plant unit. Such an area must take into account the layout constraints such as maintenance, access and safety noted in Part I Section 3.2.2. For example, if the unit is a heat exchanger with 4.8m long tubes the clearance at the channel end of the exchanger, required for the removal of the tube bundle, would be 6.4m. In addition 2.4m should be left in front of the shell cover and 0.9m each side of the shell. Therefore the plot area required for this unit is 13.6m by 2.6m for an exchanger with a 0.8m shell. A cut-out is produced for every unit that is to be located, and each unit should be numbered as for the Process Flow Diagram. The actual position and size of the unit should be marked on the cut-out, as shown in *Figure 12*).

The cut-outs are laid out on a board the surface of which should be crosshatched. The plot area is marked, to scale, together with the position of the major pipe runs and access roads, if these are to be fixed. When positioning plant units the maintenance areas are over-lapped so that units may be compactly located without compromising on maintenance and access areas, (see *Figure 13*).

Should the cut-out only consist of the item of equipment similar area surrounding the item must be left clear.

To visualise the layout problem, the two dimensional scale tem-plates, or scale cut-outs of unit areas, and equipment within each area, are shifted about the paper. A group of engineers will work

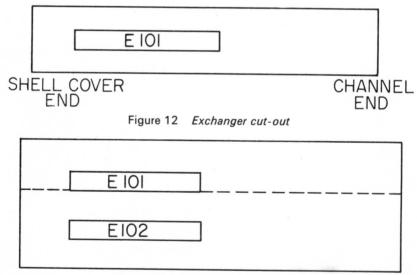

Figure 12   *Exchanger cut-out*

Figure 13   *Overlapping of cut-outs*

together with this method, to prepare a basic plot plant from which can be prepared two dimensional arrangement drawings.

A string analogue has been found helpful to students (see *Reference 47*). String is used to represent pipework and is colour coded into three groups according to cost.

3.3.2 Block Models

These can be made from blocks of wood, cardboard or polystyrene to scale (e.g. 1 : 50) set on, but not attached to, a base board faced with scale paper. A proprietory kit may be used, to save time.

These low cost models are used chiefly to develop plot and floor plans and elevations, but should not be used for detailed piping layout. They show only the major item of equipment and major pipe racks in very simple form and in their correct relationship to each other.

The more expensive pipework should be shown, e.g. 300mm, n.b. mild steel, and larger. Buildings, control rooms, switch rooms, roads and turn-outs should also be indicated. A finished model is illustrated in *Figure 14*.

This type of model may be used for proving the proposed plot plan and should ensure that all constraints on the layout have been followed. It also accomplishes the basic planning for location of related equipment for economical pipe runs.

Figure 14   *Block layout model (by courtesy of Woodall Duckham Ltd.)*

3.3.3 Drawings

The technique described in Part I Sections 3.1 to 3.3.2 are concerned with the development and evaluation of layouts. This work is done as an integral and vital part of the plant design; it correlates basic project information on equipment and site conditions and provides the source data for a final agreed layout to be used by all project design engineers. The layout techniques are shown as activities (3, 7), (7, 11), (11, 13), in *Figure 8*. In this figure the interrelated activities of mechanical, electrical, instrumental and civil engineering can be seen.

When a satisfactory layout has been reached by the layout studies, the need arises for an accurate specification of the arrangement, relative positions and dimensions of the plant items so that all design can be based on common reference documents. These show plan and elevations of the layout and specify elevation dimensions to datum points for plants on a site or equipment in a plant.

Site Layout Drawings   These show an overall plan of the site with dimensions defining property boundaries, roads, railways, process units, warehouses, buildings, pipe racks, culverts, power cables, telephone lines, carparks etc. Landscaping should be indicated where important. If the site is reasonably level around the plant areas it is not necessary to show an elevation through the site; it will be sufficient to indicate spot heights of key points above site datum level. Contours should be shown where the site is uneven. A grid north direction should be established by relating the longest straight road or building to its nearest cardinal compass point. This north should appear on every plan drawn on the project. A site datum should be established (usually called 100.00m). All other levels, whether above or below, should be related to this datum. Reference must be made on the drawing relating site datum to a true datum. On large sites the site plan can carry a grid system to identify and locate plant areas quickly. A detailed site layout drawing is essential for works reference and cannot be dispensed with in any circumstances, (see *Figure 15*).

Plot Plans and Layout Elevations   These drawings (see *Figures 16* and *17*) show to a larger scale and in more detail the arrangement and elevations of plants on a site. Plot plans should be drawn with grid north in the same orientation as defined on the site plan. Levels must be given for every item of equipment. Finished floor levels must also be specified. If plant is installed in buildings internal dimensions and door dimensions must be shown. Where steel structures are needed, positions of main steel members should be shown and any areas where steelwork cannot be allowed must be marked. Access areas, corridors,

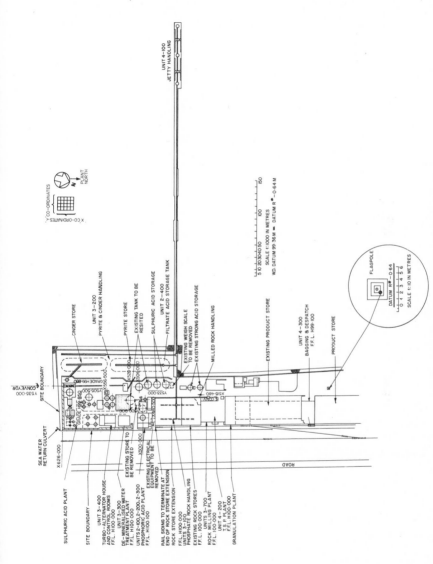

Figure 15   Typical site layout drawing

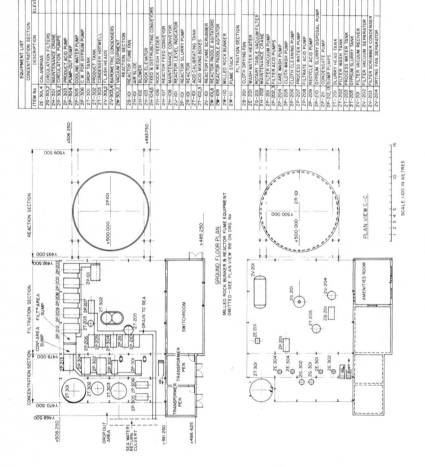

Figure 16 Typical plot plan

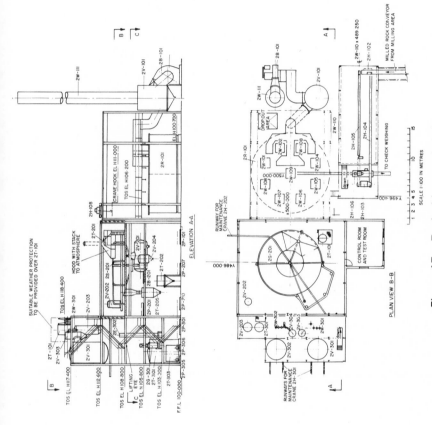

Figure 17　*Typical layout elevation*

stairways and ladders must be shown. If a plant and piping model is to be made for later design stages the plot plans and elevations can be left as simple, accurate specification drawings but if no model is made, more detail must be shown to supplement the outline dimensions and pictorial data.

3.3.4 Piping Models

These models are prepared to give an accurate detailed layout of process piping and utilities, and control facilities (See *Figure 18*).

Scale is generally not less than 1 : 30, and the model should at least show all piping of 50mm, N.B. and above. According to the design policy all pipework including instrument pipe runs may be included.

The cost of a design model for chemical and allied types of plants can be up to 0.5 % of the total installed plant cost. This should be considered as part of the total design cost and not as an addition to that cost.

The main uses are as follows:

1) Establishing optimum piping arrangements
2) Saving costs in drawing time
3) Preventing pipe fouls
4) Positioning instruments, cable racks, access platforms, lighting, etc.
5) Planning of construction
6) Use on construction site
7) Operator training
8) Exhibition and advertising

It serves as an immediate source of reference during discussions between drawing office, project, construction and maintenance engineers, safety officers and works personnel etc.

Basically there are three systems for the representation of pipework:

1) Butyrate plastic full bore system, which consists of fittings and valves true to scale, joined into or onto tubes representing the pipe.
2) Centre-line system, using brass wire to represent the centre line of the pipe with discs to represent the outside diameter. Fittings and equipment are soldered to the wire.
3) Centre-Line System using plastic covered wire in a variety of colours and having plastic clip-on sleeves to represent the overall diameter of pipe plus lagging and also to carry the same valves used in *1)*. Both *1)* and *3)* eliminate the painting of colour code,

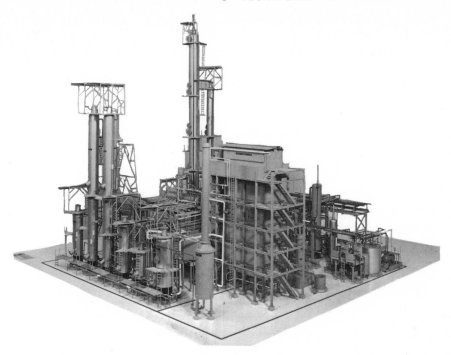

Figure 18   *Piping model (by courtesy of Woodhall Duckham Ltd.)*

provide realistic valves and fittings and eliminate the need for a soldering iron as welding by solvent is used.

Base boards may be constructed of 13mm chip board, stiffened underneath as necessary, and top painted matt grey or preferably have a plastic faced graph finish consistent with the model scale. When, due to the size of the plot, multiple base boards are required, they should be tongued or dowelled for alignment.

Items of equipment may be constructed in wood, plastic or metal. Main flanges, davits and manholes are usually shown. Pipe gantries and racks are normally constructed from plastic or wood. Care should be taken on the finished detail and appearance. It should be of robust construction with all equipment steelwork, pipework and racks securely fixed in position.

The decision to build a detailed model should be made at the outset of a contract. As an integral part of the design include it in the critical path analysis of a contract. The equipment information must be available early otherwise the value of the model as a design tool is largely lost, since it follows on after engineering design rather than guiding it.

When a whole plant does not justify a model, it may be advisable to model just one section such as a complicated junction of pipe-racks or extensive alloy pipework at towers. Where future expansion is known the equipment may be modelled and differently coloured from the rest to show that it will be installed later.

To identify items on the model it is suggested that a colour code be used. It cannot agree in detail with the British Standard 1710 (see *Reference 43*) because the range of coloured plastic piping for modelling purposes is limited to approximately 12 colours. The colour code used must be indicated on the model.

A suggested colour code scheme might be:

Roadways and access	Black
Electric motors	Orange
Pumps, compressors, machinery	Black
Steelwork	Grey
Pipe bridges and racks	Black
Foundations and concrete	Buff
platforms and walkways	Aluminium
Vessels, towers, heat exchangers	
1) Insulated	White
2) Uninsulated	Grey
3) Skirts to vessels	Black
4) Supports or saddles	Grey
Tanks	Black
Baseboards	Grey
Piping	
1) Process lines or gas	Red
2) Chemicals	Blue
3) Inert or purge gas	Orange
4) Steam	Yellow
5) Water	Green

6) On all insulated lines a white snap-on sleeve will indicate insulation

7) All valves on line	Grey

8) Underground pipes and trenches will be shown as dotted lines on the baseboard.

    Reference See References 44–48 on Models for Plant Layout.

3.4 Computers

If there are six alternative positions for each of one of six blocks (representing equipment) then there are 720 (6!) feasible combinations of these six blocks. Clearly for a chemical plant which contains many more blocks it is not practicable to examine all alternatives even using computers. Thus in general for computerised layout of chemical plant the judgement of the engineer has to be combined with the calculation power of the computer.

Computer usage has been mainly on evaluation of systematic techniques and it has been shown that small problems can be handled manually with the various correlation and compatibility methods described in Part I Section 3.2. However, as the problems increase in size the time required to solve them becomes longer and it may take days to generate and evaluate all the possible layouts. A brief mention follows of some of the programmes which have been reported in the literature. It is hoped that this may assist the reader who wishes to study the subject in more depth.

CRAFT 'Computerised Relative Allocation of Facilities Technique', by Armour Buffa and Vollman (see *Reference 1*) is a program which used a simulation alogorithm which arranges departments in a given plant area. Input into the algorithm includes the area of the individual departments or plant units, handling volume in unit loads moved between departments and handling cost per unit load per unit distance between pairs of departments. The unit cost is established in advance and is independent of the plant arrangement; which is often not true in practice. The programme determines distances between departments in any arrangement and from this using the handling cost matrix, seeks minimum cost for exchanges of department locations. The exchange is repeated until minimum cost is found.

ALDEP 'Automated Layout Design Program', by Evans (see *Reference 3*), is a program which applies a heuristic programming method to create block layouts. Input to the programme includes the area requirements of each department or unit and preference table which is a matrix of weighting factors which indicate the desirability of units to be near each other. These weighting factors can be given values by the user to represent his view of their relative importance. The programme will layout up to three floors. It performs a two step process for each floor of the building—first, any non-assigned department's area is allocated to specific floors and second, those departments assigned to a floor are given a specific location on that floor. A department is randomly selected and processed, then the preference table for that department is searched to find any department with a performance of highest priority which is then selected. When all departments have been processed the resulting layout is scored and printed out. By selecting block layouts with highest scores the best layouts are obtained for further analysis.

CORLAP 'Computerised Relationship Layout Planning', by Lee and Moore (see *Reference 5*) is a programme which requires input in the form of Relationship Chart as described by Munther (see *Reference 7*); the departmental area restrictions; the size of the unit square to be manipulated and the maximum ratio of building to width. The main algorithm consists of a heuristic programme which adds departments in a logical fashion to generate a block plan layout. The output consists of a matrix print-out representing the block plan.

A programme for the layout of plant modules with inter-connecting piping has been described by Gunn (see *Reference 4*). The objective function considered is the cost of the interconnecting piping and the cost of the building. For each module co-ordinates of the nozzles to which piping is attached are input to the programme together with the datum co-ordinates of the modules, pipe descriptions and costs per unit length of pipe. The co-ordinates of the plant modules are changed so that the objective function is minimised. Minimum and maximum constraints are set on the co-ordinates of the modules so that they do not occupy the same volume in space. Accurate positions of the nozzles and plant modules are available at the end of the computation and may be used in further design work.

The analytical approach to solving location and layout problems has been discussed in depth by Reed (see *Reference 8*). Methods exist which enable mathematical models to be made, but unless the problem is heavily constrained the amount of computation required to generate and evaluate alternatives demands the use of large computers. Current work is aimed at developing algorithms which will reduce the computation load. The engineers' contribution must be to develop constraint data by quantifying maintenance and operability requirements.

Staff at the Computer Aided Design Centre (CAD) Cambridge, have examined methods of applying computer graphics to the layout problem (see *Reference 6*). The designer indicates via a light pen and display a layout of a plant area in which a re-arrangement of the vessels might lead to a reduction in costs. Using the light pen the user may then interchange vessels until visual optimisation of the area is achieved. In addition the user is able to specify areas of space which are considered favourable for routing pipes and the routing algorithms find minimal routes subject to these constraints.

Bush and Wells (see *Reference 2*) have used an interactive graphics facility to produce unit plot plans. Equipment shape is generated on the screen together with a box indicating the constraints on the layout. Pipe-work is self-generated between equipment according to the input data. Different brightness is used to indicate the more expensive runs. Adjustment to the plan is carried out using a light pen. The approximate costs of the pipe runs are generated and a manual search is carried out until a satisfactory design is achieved.

References   See References 1–8 on Computerised Layout of Plant.

4 APPENDIX TO PART I

4.2 Typical Clearances between Various Units for Preliminary Site Layouts

		m
Plant areas		15
Boilers and furnaces	to the adjacent	15
Blowdown stacks with flares	unit, main roads	30
Gas holders	or boundary	30
Cooling towers		30
Effluent plants		15
Loading areas		15
Warehouses		30
Offices and canteens	to process units	30
Medical centres		30
Garages		30
Fire station		30
Workshops		30
Main roads		12
Main roads	to building line	9
Paths	excluding loading	1.5
Railroads	bays	15
Railroads		2.5
Roads	centre line to	7
Paved areas and paths	loading bay	4
Railroads	headroom	4.6

Note: For detailed layout each case should be judged on its particular merits.

4.1 Typical Areas and Sizes for Preliminary Site Layouts

Administration	10m²	per administration employee
Workshop	20m²	per workshop employee
Laboratory	20m²	per laboratory employee
Canteen	1m²	per dining place
	3.5m²	per place including kitchen and store
Medical centre	0.10—0.15m²	per employee depending on complexity of service
	minimum 10m²	
Fire Station	500m²	per site
(housing 1 fire, 1 crash, 1 foam, 1 generator and 1 security vehicle)		
Garage (including maintenance)	100m²	per vehicle
Main roads	10m	wide
Side roads	7.5m	wide
Pathways	1.2m	wide up to 10 people a minute
	2m	wide over 10 people a minute (e.g. near offices, canteens and bus stops)
Road turning circles	90° turn	11m radius
	'T' junct.	7.5m radius
	minor roads	4m radius
Minimum railroad curve	56m	inside curve radius
Cooling towers per tower	0.04m²/kWh	(mechanical draught)
	to 0.08m²/kWh	(natural draught)

4.3 Typical Constraint Allowances for Preliminary Plant Layout*

EQUIPMENT	SAFETY	ELEVATION	HORIZONTAL	VERTICAL	CONSTRUCTION/ERECTION/GEN.
CENTRIFUGES CRUSHERS MILLS			3m	2m+λ	5m access corridor
DRYERS			1.5m+λ	2m+λ	2.5m to building walls
COLUMNS			1.5m		3m between adjacent columns 40m² packing storage
FURNACES AND FIRED HEATERS	15m to hazard		3m		2 widths (centre to centre adjacent heaters)
REACTORS STIRRED VESSELS	15m to hazard		1.5m	3m+λ	4m access area 40m² for each 1000 ft³ reator volume

REBOILERS:	1.5m + λ channel 2m shell 1.5m sides	1.5m
HEAT EXCHANGER HORIZ.	check column	
TANKS	Bund volume of largest tank 15m to hazard	½ diam. (av) between tanks · 3m
PUMPS	N.P.S.H. check back to equipment	2m motor end 1.5m sides
FILTERS	3m if solids dump	1.5m + λ
COMPRESSORS	1.5m + λ	3m + λ · 2 widths (centre to centre adjacent compressors)

λ is the length of the longest internal part of the equipment that must be removed for maintenance or operation

* note these values need to be checked when laying out in detail

Taken from—M. J. Bush—Ph.D. Thesis, Sheffield University 1971

Part II

1 LAYOUT OF PLANT ITEMS

1.1 Plant Vessels

1.1.1 Reactors

Reactions may be carried out in a wide variety of vessels which may include simple non-agitated vessel, jacketted agitated autoclave, vertical mixer reactor with internal or external heat transfer surface, horizontal agitated heat exchanger reactor, ball mill reactor, fluidised bed reactor complete with lift pipes system and regenerator, fixed bed tubular reactors, also in tubular furnaces, which are discussed in Part II Section 1.2

For the purpose of layout of chemical plant, reactors are divided into the following broad classifications:

1) Continuous non-catalytic reactors
2) Batch reactors
3) Solid catalyst reactors — fixed bed
4) Solid catalyst reactors — moving bed

Continuous Non-Catalytic Reactors The simplest form is a vertical vessel, usually agitated, with heat transfer by an external jacket, internal coils or external exchanger.

Jacketted vessels present no special layout problem.

To assist in removing an internal heat transfer coil through a flanged connection at the top of the vessel a platform should be provided. If the coil is heavy, then a monorail connection is needed.

External heat exchangers, operating without a circulating pump, only require that high temperature piping should be kept as short as possible to reduce dangers of leakages and explosions, whilst having sufficient bends and pipe lengths to limit pipe stresses. With a circulating pump the reactor, unless under pressure, must be elevated to

63

give the necessary NPSH. For vessels subject to expansion the nozzle connecting to the pump suction is nearest to the fixed supports.

Reactor agitators are almost always top mouted, so that space must be allowed on top of the reactor for maintenance. For bottom mounted agitators, the reactor must be elevated sufficiently, both for maintenance and complete withdrawal. Reactors in the form of a shell and tube horizontal heat exchanger with an agitator at one end are mounted as for a pump and heat exchanger combination, on a single base plate together with the agitator drive. They should be on ground level wherever possible.

Relatively high pressures and temperatures can be associated with reactors which are then called autoclaves. They are generally thick walled vessels kept to a minimum elevation due to their weight. Vertical autoclaves are often supported by lugs located some way up the vessel walls as this can reduce pipe stressing problems. The supports are preferable mounted on concrete because of the temperature involved and to damp out any vibrations.

Horizontal autoclaves are laid out with access at both ends for maintenance of the agitator and drive mechanism.

Ball mill reactors are laid out as any normal ball mill (Part II Section 1.9) except that they are generally contained inside a hot-air jacket, and space should be allowed for the air ducting around the mill.

Packed tubes reactors are elevated so that the old packing can be dumped into a truck or conveyor beneath it. Similarly an overhead hoist should be provided for filling, together with a platform at the top of the reactor. The filling may be automatically performed.

Batch Reactors   The remarks in the previous section also apply to batch reactors. In addition operating access is a more important factor in layout (see *Figure 19*). Platforms are particularly needed for viewing the contents through sight glasses, for cleaning and for manual addition of materials. In the last case, lifting devices should be provided to lift the chemicals from floor level and there should be space near the reactor for the delivery and temporary storage of these materials. Often the additions are made via a chute from the next floor. For cleaning purposes services such as lighting, steam and water should be conveniently placed and space for waste bins should be allowed to the side of the platform. Extra ventilation during cleaning may have to be provided. Special attention should be paid to floor drainage if frequent cleaning is necessary.

The smaller batch processes often require that the whole reactor be removed and replaced by another. This allows maintenance or awkward cleaning to be done with the minimum interruption to produc-

Figure 19   *Access to reactors (by courtesy of Lightnin Mixers.)*

tion. If a glass lining fails in service, usually the only recourse is to replace the equipment. Batch processing can often run in 'campaigns' of different products. It may be necessary to rearrange the reactors etc. between campaigns. The building should be arranged with floor openings right up the building so that any item may be removed, and lowered directly to the ground. It is good practice to support the reactors on split rings so that removal is carried out by dropping the vessel down to the floor below. This avoids the necessity of excessive headroom above the vessel, and the need for multi-directional movement.

Multiple product reactors are not always permanently piped up. The services are brought to convenient manifolds and connected to the reactors by hoses. Then one reactor is connected to the next by flexible connections according to the particular requirements of the current product. It is essential to place the manifolds and reactors in relation to one another so that the hoses neither foul walkways nor lifting shafts. Often in such a situation each reactor may be hard piped to its own exchangers, condenser and even to its own centrifuge or filter to form a reactor unit and the flexible connection made between such units. Layout has to be considered within each unit and for the relation between units. Vessel ventilation ducts should be so arranged that flowback of dangerous fumes into other vessels is avoided.

Solid Catalyst Reactors—Fixed Bed   This type of reactor is packed with catalyst either in bulk between supports inside the reactor vessel, or within tubes or baskets. They should be kept at ground level wherever possible due to their weight and for accessibility during operation and maintenance. The elevation will be decided by the method adopted to remove the spent catalyst.

For bottom removal designs, the reactors must be elevated sufficiently to allow catalyst transfer by either mechanical transport, belt conveyor, or hand trucks depending on the quantity. Catalysts may also be removed by pneumatic or dense phase conveying. For loading, small quantities can be handled with a davit and winch, larger quantities require a monorail and air operated hoise, while still larger amounts might need a skip hoist or pneumatic conveyor. Reactors containing top removable internals, or catalyst must have access platforms and sufficient clear space (at least 2m sq.) above the reactor for the operator to work safely and efficiently. Removal of catalyst or internals from side manholes is carried out manually and only requires platform working space (2m sq. minimum) around the bottom of each manhole. In all cases at least 4m sq. must be left at the base of each reactor for transport and temporary holding of both fresh and spent catalyst. This space is very dependent on the catalyst exchange procedure in which guidance must be sought from the operating department concerned.

Reactors run in series or parallel, can have common support overhead structures and one lifting device such as a monorail to serve all the reactors. Often the same overhead structure can be used for loading catalyst and for removing internals. Similar space at the base of the reactors can be saved when they are grouped together. Spacing between reactors must allow thermal expansion of interconnecting piping.

Solid Catalyst Reactors—Moving Bed This category of reactors includes those where the bed is transferred from the reactor for purposes of regeneration and also fluidised bed reactors in which non catalytic processes take place, (see *Figure 20*).

With the first type reactor the height of the base of the regenerator is determined by the discharge angle of the outlet pipe from the base outlet hopper of the regenerator to the conveyor inlet boot in order to obtain free solid flow. Similarly the top of the conveyor should be as low as possible consistent with the angle of the pipe conveyor discharge point to the reactor inlet. Placing the conveyor boot in an underground pit to reduce the overall height should be avoided if possible. The lift pipes, seal legs, etc., designed to suit the fluid mechanics of the particular system will greatly influence relative elevating.

Very substantial structural designs are involved with moving bed

Figure 20   *Moving bed column showing conveyor (by courtesy of Courtaulds Engineering Ltd.)*

reactors due to the heavy weights and high elevations involved. All equipment must be properly supported with due regard to the thermal expansions and dynamic loading.

The layout of fluidised bed reactors generally follows that of fixed bed reactors but account must be taken of the associated fluid/solid separation equipment and fans (see Part II Sections 1.11 and 1.5.3).

1.1.2 Mixers

Mixers are divided into those for processing solids or pastes and those for handling liquids. Equipment used for mixing solids into liquids comes under the category of liquid mixers, while that used for mixing liquids into solids falls within the solid mixer category.

Solids Mixers   The first group of the solids mixers contains those having a rotor within a stationary container, such as the ribbon, the single and double rotor mixers and the planetary type. Materials are fed in at the top of the mixer or at one end and the product is removed either from the middle or the opposite end at the bottom of the mixer. The conveyor feeding the materials can be laid out above the mixer from any plan angle with a chute discharge placed at the correct slope to allow free flow of material. The layout of the discharge side is made in a similar fashion.

In mixers having heating or cooling, provision must be made for the necessary piping connections, valves and instrumentation. In all cases space must be allowed for opening the equipment in order to clean the agitator and casing, and to remove the agitator completely for maintenance.

Solids may also be mixed by a pneumatic mixer which can have a subsidiary rotor. Space is needed for the cyclone above the mixer.

The second group contains those having a flat horizontal pan with vertical mullers on the surface of the pan. Feeding is from the top, discharge from the bottom, but since those mixers are almost always without a cover, there is no problem of access to the inside of the mixing pan. A monorail or hoist should be provided to enable the whole muller turret to be removed for maintenance.

The third group of solids mixers are conically shaped rotating tumblers. Feeding is through covered holes in the top of the drum (while it is stationary) and access platforms need to be provided in the case of large mixers. Apart from occasional cleaning of the inside of the drum there are no internals to be maintained.

Paste mixers can be vertical, horizontal or angular types. Some have hinged agitators for drum removal and agitator cleaning. Kneader and Banbury type mixers are heavily built horizontal machines.

They should be sited on firm foundations, preferably at ground level. They can be fed by hand or by conveyor and for the former, local storage is needed. If they tip for emptying, the travel should not be fouled by pipeways etc., nor should it extend into gangways. Space is needed for removing heavy internals for maintenance.

Liquid Mixers   Liquids mixers are tanks having vertical, angular and sometimes horizontal agitators mounted in them. The most common type consists of a vertical tank and a top mounted vertical impeller unit.

Access to manholes and to the agitator drive mechanism should be provided on the large tanks, as well as the space to remove the whole agitator system. Such space can be saved by using a split shaft with a coupling connection. However, couplings are a source of dynamic inbalance, which is costly to eliminate.

Groups of mixing tanks can be laid out in a straight line, in pairs, or staggered. The last arrangement is particularly useful when laying out pairs of connected mixer-settlers, since it enables the tanks to be physically close together, and gives the shortest practical connections between tanks. Gravity flow mixer-settler arrangements have sloped launders or pipes connecting each pair, and it is necessary to provide sufficient head for gravity flow. Short connections are desirable to minimise differences in elevation. Other types of mixer-settlers include the 'box' arrangement of horizontal rectangular boxes with mixers in alternate ends of the vessels, which mix and pump at the same time, thus eliminating the need for differences in elevation. As they tend to be rather long, sufficient space must be provided for erection. Otherwise maintenance and access is as described above.

Mixer type reactors have been already described earlier in this Section.

Thickeners   Thickeners are large diameter horizontal tanks having slow rotating sludge rakes mounted inside the tank. Slurry is fed by pipe to the feed well in the centre of the tank, the clean liquor is removed via a peripheral launder and outlet pipe, while the sludge is taken out from the centre bottom of the tank, usually by a screw conveyor. Due to their large diameter, thickeners are often placed out of doors and away from the main process in order not to take up valuable process space. Thickeners have a superstructure across the top of the tank to give support and allow access to the drive mechanism and feed well, while maintenance of the sludge rake is carried out in situ, after emptying the tank.

Continuous counter-current decantation is frequently carried out with thickeners. In this case, differences in elevation between the first and subsequent thickeners are made in the layout to allow gravity flow from one to the next. On account of civil costs use should be made of natural variations in ground level.

1.1.3 Evaporators

The minimum height of an evaporator is set by the NPSH requirement of the product pump. It is not good practice to put the pump in a pit to obtain the required NPSH although it can be done. A pump should not be placed directly under the evaporator as it is sometimes necessary to lower the calandria.

Barometric legs should be at least 10m from the vessel base to the level in the barometric sump. This is usually situated on the ground floor. Horizontal sections should be avoided in barometric legs and ideally legs should be perpendicular. Preferably sight glasses, instruments and sample points should have access platforms. Platforms should also be provided, for cleaning purposes, at manholes, allowing 4sq.m of free platform per manhole opening. Further platforms may be needed for bundle cleaning and repair together with hoisting equipment. Room must be left for the use of mechanical tube cleaners (when required) and for the removal and replacement of tubes. This may mean having a removable panel in the roof above the evaporator. Space may be provided for additional pipework and valves so that one evaporator can be blanked off for repairs and cleaning while the others remain on stream. For chemical cleaning room must be left, usually on the ground floor, for the cleaning liquor tanks and pumps. It may be necessary to provide additional ventilation during cleaning due to toxic fumes etc.

For multiple-effect evaporators it is desirable to place the individual effects as close as possible to minimise vapor lines. However space must be allowed for insulation and its maintenance. Vapour liquid separators should be accommodated in the layout without increasing the distance between effects. It is better to stagger the effects at 60° centres in parallel rows or have a simple 'U'. The 60° desired layout allows one pan to be cut out as the vapour pipes can be easily rearranged. The structure and access platforms should be common for all the effects.

Where spillages are liable to occur the floor should be bunded and drainings channelled to the effluent pit for sampling and necessary treatment.

As vapour piping is always of large diameter, it is necessary that layout of the evaporators is not finalised until the detailed pipe layout has been executed. In this detail future plant expansion should be considered, i.e. whether an extra effect will be added, or whether extra heat transfer surface will be added to each evaporator either internally or externally with circulation pumps.

A typical evaporator layout is shown in *Figure 21*.

1.1.4 Crystallisers

Some crystallisers are similar to evaporators in construction and in their ancillary equipment. Otherwise there are the agitated batch crystallisers which can be treated as mixing vessels, the double pipe crystallisers which can be laid out as heat exchangers, and the trough type continuous crystalliser which is comparable to a ribbon mixer.

Layout requirements for crystallisers are similar to those for evaporators but there are often additional agitators. For slurry piping care must be taken to use long radius elbows and to provide plenty of clean-out facilities. Such pipes should be sloped for ease of drainage.

While it is desirable to place the crystallisers as close as possible to one another, the use of horizontal heaters or coolers often precludes this, due to the placing of the exchanger between the crystallisers. On

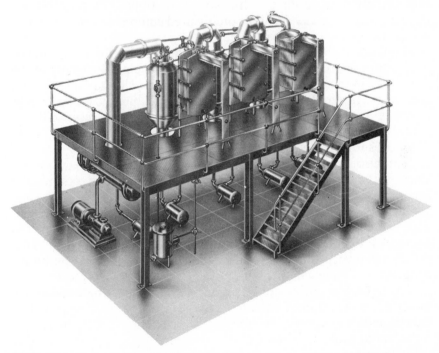

Figure 21   *Layout of multi-effect evaporators (by courtesy of APV Company Ltd.)*

the other hand vertical exchangers need not as they can be placed above the crystallisers.

A large number of crystallisers can be arranged either all in one row or in a double bank with the separators and heat exchangers located between the two rows. This leaves the outside of the double bank completely clear, and allows one central platform for easy operation and access. This results in a neat piping arrangement with very short connections.

1.2 Furnaces and Fired Equipment

The first consideration in the layout of fired equipment is safety and a thorough study should be made of local and specific codes and standards. The general rule is that fired equipment should be located at least 15m away from other equipment which could be a source of spillage or leakage of gas. Underground drain points and manhole covers should be sealed within the furnace vicinity, i.e. 12m measured horizontally from furnace walls. No pits or trenches should be permitted to extend under furnaces or any fired equipment and in general should be avoided in furnace areas.

The location of fired equipment may depend on the raw material flow from the previous stage or storage, and the product flow to the next stage in the process. Furnace transfer lines should be short and consideration should be given to common stack policy. Other factors affecting location are disposal liquid effluents, the gaseous effluent relative to the other plants and the neighbourhood, and the proximity of services for the fired equipment.

Ventilation should be provided in the working area particularly where sulphur-bearing fuels are used and high temperatures may be experienced.

Furnaces should be spaced about two widths apart (centre to centre). They should be arranged with the centre line of the stacks on the common line wherever possible and the stacks should be located at the end or side which is away from the unit. Economics or air pollution control will dictate whether single or common stacks are required for groups of heaters; from a plant layout point of view single stacks are preferred as they do not box the furnaces in with breeching pieces to the common stack, with the consequent problem of access by cranes for tube removal.

In the arrangement of furnaces, care should be taken that there is ample room at the firing front for the operation of the burners, and for burner control panel, if required. In the case of bottom floor fired furnaces this would mean adequate head room (2.5m) underneath the furnace. In the case of wall fired furnaces a platform width of at least 1m with escape routes at each end is required. With top fired furnaces adequate exit routes from each end of the furnace are necessary, one of which must be a stairway. Peepholes and observation doors should only be provided where absolutely necessary. They need only be reached by means of a fixed ladder if less than 4m above grade, but at greater heights, platforms are required.

Access is needed for relining, tube removal and other repairs. The roof clearance has to be consistent with crane and lift requirements and the support structures should not interfere with maintenance. Platforms are needed for maintenance of soot blowers.

1.3 Columns

Elevation Considerations   The height relationship of the column to reboiler in thermosyphon reboilers and the column to bottoms pump for NPSH requirements are set by fluid flow; all other relationships between the column and associated items are determined by the designer. It is convenient to have the condenser above the column head to minimise vapour piping and provide gravity reflux. This arrangement demands support for the reflux drum etc., and requires an adequate head in the condenser cooling water circuit. The alternative arrangement of low level condenser requires pumped reflux, longer vapour lines and care in layout to provide adequate NPSH for the reflux and bottoms pumps but saves structures and water piping. The choice is solely economic.

Where columns are of very small diameter (<0.3m) or form part of a plant requiring a building/structure for other reasons, it is normally preferable to use supported columns. Otherwise the self-supporting column is normally the cheapest form of construction. These are mounted on a skirt at ground level.

It may be cheaper for small columns to be elevated to a height in excess of the normal requirements to allow gravity flow to a following vessel or the reduce piping length.

Access   On columns above 0.5m diameter segmented platforms with ladders are usually attached to the column shell where carbon steel or thick stainless steel is used for construction. The use of thin wall stainless steel titanium (3mm and lower) or normal thickness non-ferrous materials prohibits attachment of platforms and these columns usually require a structure for support. The maximum allowable straight run of ladder before a rest platform is 10m, but 6m is more desirable. Safety loops should always be used on ladders more than 2.5m high. If access is required to a high level condenser system, a supporting/access structure must be considered, or these items and the access structure must be carried from the column.

External access to the column itself is usually required for inspection manholes, packing branches on packed columns and to piping/instrument connections. Platforms for access to level gauges and controllers should not be installed if the underside of the supporting steelwork is less than normal headroom clearance. Access may be made to tower platforms from adjacent floor level but the tower platform should also be provided with an alternative means of escape.

Where self-supporting columns are used, access for major maintenance work such as painting, insulation or attention to main flanged joints is usually provided by bosun's chair or temporary scaffolding. Room for these must be allowed for in the layout around the column base and it is also useful to fit cleats on the shell to facilitate scaffold erection.

Provision for internal access should be made to allow cleaning, tray setting, corrosion inspection, levelling of packing supports, and other general maintenance items. Below about 0.5m diameter internal access is not practicable and the column should be flanged in about 2.5m lengths and broken down for internal attention.

On larger columns above 0.5m access can be provided by normal size manholes (460mm). In tray columns it is usual to leave a removable section in each tray which can be removed and thus form an access way between trays. It is preferable to design this access such that a man enters the top of the works downwards when removing tray segments. For packed columns similar manholes are used for packing, installation and replacement. The centre line of manholes will normally be 1m above platform elevation but may be varied between 0.5m and 1.3m. Manholes are preferentially placed outwards from the central pipeway or structure, and any dropping area to allow for the removal of tower attachments, internals or packing should be on the side of the column away from the piperack. Davits should be provided for lifting and holding manholes covers, column heads, or similar large, heavy items intended to be removed during maintenance. Adequate clearance must be left for the swing of the manhole cover on its davit and entrance to manhole must not be obstructed by piping.

Generally, columns are considerably higher than most other items of equipment and in cases where they are delivered complete should have adequate access, unloading space and erection space (see *Figure 3*). For this reason they are best located when possible toward one end of the process area. In cases where they are site fabricated an area will be required for material storage or sub-assembly welding near to the ultimate location. The siting should be carefully considered so that special lifts or testing procedure do not hold up work on other equipment.

Lifting points should be provided on all columns (except the very smallest) for ease of erection—these lifting points are best placed above the centre of gravity of the column or column section.

Spacing   About 3m minimum should be allowed between columns and this may need to be increased if frequent tray replacement is envisaged. For extremely high columns for which special foundation designs are necessary, the area required for foundations may be the criterion in spacing, Wind interaction could also influence the disposition of adjacent columns.

Adjacent columns should be checked, so that platforms do not overlap and that 1m space minimum is left between column foundation and plinth. A clear space must be provided by each column for the drop out of internals and attachments, and complete clearance should be allowed for the davits at the top of the column if provided. On packed columns this space should also allow for installation and maintenance of packing.

Special consideration should be given to equipment operating at very high or low temperatures due to the increased insulation thickness.

1.4 Exchangers

The first consideration in the layout is normally process flow, see Part I, Section 2.1. However where there are a large number of exchangers, they are often put together in one or more groups. By this means savings are often possible on service pipework, pipebridges, structural steelwork and in the provisions of lifting and other maintenance facilities but may entail additional process piping and access steelwork. An economic balance has to be struck and the location should result in a layout which is convenient and comfortable to operate and maintain.

Grouped exchangers should be in rows with the axes of channel

Figure 22 *Typical distillation column layout (by courtesy of ICI Ltd.)*

nozzles in a common vertical plane to present a neat appearance and to make pipe detailing easier. Exchangers may be stacked but never more than three high if mutually supported. Special cases arise for fin tube units and air cooled exchangers.

Horizontal clearance of at least 1.5m should be left between exchangers or exchangers and piping. Where space is limited clearance may be reduced between alternate exchangers but in no case should the clearance over insulation between channel flanges be less than 0.6m.

Unless a heat exchanger is to be removed as a whole for cleaning and overhaul, adequate space must be left at the ends for dismantling. At the channel end of a typical U tube or floating head exchanger about 0.6m should be allowed for removing shell and floating head covers. Thus a floating head exchanger with 5m tubes requires an installation length of approximately 12m. Facilities for pulling, lifting and supporting bundles should be available either as mobile equipment or as integral lifting gear within the structures, i.e. davits, lifting beams etc. The tube walls are the weakest part of the bundle and care should be taken to ensure that the bundle is well supported by cradles at regular intervals. Where possible, large heat exchangers should be located with suitable access to permit servicing by mobile cranes for lifting of covers and bundles, the exchanger channels preferably pointing towards the road or access area. Sometimes it is more

Figure 23   *Grouping of exchangers (by courtesy of Foster Wheeler Ltd.)*

convenient, especially with high pressure exchangers, to draw off the shell and clean the tubes in situ. However, pulled out bundles or shells should not extend over main roads. Vertical exchangers should be set to allow lifting of the tube bundle. Similar considerations apply in the case of fixed tube plate exchanger as adequate space must be left for the insertion and withdrawal of individual tubes or cleaning rods.

Most exchangers are located with base about 1m above ground level. Some exchangers have a condensate or holding pot after an outlet. In such cases piping should be arranged so that the top of the pot is at least in line with the bottom of the exchanger to avoid flooding the tubes and adversely affecting the exchanger duty. In some cases where flooding of tubes is necessary (e.g. a total condenser) the relative level of the control pot to the exchange is important and will determine the position of the exchanger. The positioning of reboilers relative to columns is discussed in Part II Section 1.3. Elevation of exchangers may be necessary because of a NPSH requirement of a following centrifugal pump. Consideration should be given to the use of side or tangential connections to reduce the heights of exchangers.

Air cooled exchangers are usually located adjacent to the plant they serve and can conveniently be mounted above other equipment. Account should be taken in siting this type of exchanger of the proximity of control rooms or other delicate instrumentation which could be adversely affected by vibration or noise.

Matrix type aluminium heat exchangers are usually so light that they can be regarded as a pipe fitting with little or no support other than from the pipework itself. Room should be available to replace the exchanger.

Layout of exchangers can have an effect on piping design and this should be carefully considered. Some examples are quoted in the reference below, which descusses inter alia layout of exchangers in detail.

Reference   See Reference 39 on Heat Exchanger Layout.

1.5 Fluid Transfer Equipment

1.5.1 Pumps

The conventional horizontal bedplate or monobloc centrifugal pump is most frequently specified for process industry use. Common variants to this design exist such as the in line, submerged, self priming or glandless pumps. Also there are many types of positive displacement which are useful in special situations. Careful assessment of all the problems of layout should be made when specifying the type of pump to be used.

Location   Buildings should not be specially provided for pumps without good reason. A shelter is justified when a group of pumps or their associated valves is visited at intervals more than once a week for operations taking longer than two minutes, or if the pumps are to be maintained more often than once per month. A room is justified when a group of pumps is frequently attended for periods greater than thirty minutes. Large pumps are normally grouped in a building for operational and maintenance convenience and to confine noise. Possible freezing of the liquid in a pump is another reason for providing a building.

Generally the elevation will be governed by the type of pump selected, and in turn on the duty and liquid pumped, but most pumps should be located above known flood height and as far as possible at ground level. Pumps which must be located below ground because of suction conditions will involve costly civil work and drainage problems. Pumps at elevated locations will generally cause vibration problems in structure design.

Pumps should, in general, be located close to the equipment from which they take suction. Changes in direction of the suction line should be at least 600mm from the pumps. Adequate space must be allowed for flow measurement or control apparatus associated with pumps.

Any reduction in suction line size required at pumps should be made with eccentric reducers, with bottom straight for pumps taking suction from above and with top straight for pumps taking suction from below. All overhead pump suction lines should be arranged to drain from the equipment towards the pump without inverted pockets.

Provision should be made to isolate the pump from the feed vessel so that it can be dismantled without draining the vessel.

Pump Arrangement   As far as possible clearances and piping should provide free access to one side of the driver and pump. Pumps should be arranged in line with drivers facing the access gangway. Double rows of pumps can be arranged with pumps back to back piped up to a common pipe bridge. Piping should be arranged alongside the pump end of the assembly; this avoids piping runs over pumps and motors and allows grouping of valves, pipe fittings and local instruments. For pumps taking feed directly from tanks the pump suction should be horizontal whereas it should be on top when drawing from an overhead pipe run. Pump discharges normally should be at the top. Groups of pumps should have their discharges and discharge valves lined up and if possible their suction valves and seal water pipes also lined up.

Clearances between pumps or pumps and piping should be at least 1.2m for small pumps (<18KW) and 1.5m to 2m for larger pumps. 2m to 2.5m should be provided for working aisles (see *Figure 24*). Clearances between pumps and walls should be at least 1.2m unless the space is used as an aisle. The aisles should be arranged so that maintenance trolleys can enter and leave the pump area without having to reverse. Doors to pump rooms should also be 2m wide to allow trolley access. Similarly the open side of shelters should be 2m wide and facing leeward of the prevailing wind.

In the open, pumps handling hot liquids ($>60°$C) should be at least 7.5m from pumps handling volatile liquids (b.p.$<40°$C). In pump rooms they should be separated by a vapour-tight wall.

Roof Clearances and Lifting Beams   Means of lifting should be provided for pumps or motors weighing more than 25kg. This can be either a fixed lifting beam or portable 'A' frame. Lifting beams should run from the pump to the centre of the nearest aisle, and their use should not be hindered by pipework. It should be possible to place and use 'A' frames without interference from pipework.

Figure 24 *Layout of main pump bay allowing ready access for inspection and maintenance (Photograph by courtesy of BP and of Matthew Hall Engineering Ltd.)*

Roof clearance should be a minimum of 2.5m and should be increased to 3.5m if 'A' frames are used. For small pumps allow a minimum clearance distance of 1.5 times the maximum height of pump for removal of parts.

Floor and Drainage Pumps should stand on plinths raised at least 150mm above the floor. No part of the pump or motor should overhang its plinth. Multiple pumps can stand on the same plinth, which should then be graded (1 in 120) to allow spillages to drain away. The drainage from pump beds plates should be at the pump and away from the motor into drain points or gullies. The floor should be provided with a fall (1 in 120) so that washings and spillages drain into the nearest gully. These gullies should be connected to the correct factory effluent system.

Electrics Starters and cables should be in the same relative positions to each motor. All pumps should have a local stop button provided for emergency use. Large or functionally important units should always be started from controls near the unit to ensure safe and reliable starting.

Starters should be situated at the edge of the aisles in sight of the pumps they control and/or their pressure gauges. Starters should be heights 1.2m to 1.8m above floor level.

1.5.2 Compressors

Reciprocating   Reciprocating compressors should be located on foundations independent of any building or pipe trestles. Similarly anchors and restraints for pipes adjacent to the reciprocating compressors should be independent of any other structures or buildings.

Large reciprocating compressors (especially those for natural gas) should be elevated above grade with plate or grid flooring at the level of the top of the foundation for operating and maintenance. The height of these false floors above ground level should be kept to a minimum consistent with the adequacy of the space for the piping and access especially to valves and drains and also to provide height for degassing lube and seal oil. The reciprocating gas compressor suction and discharge headers should be located at ground level.

Spacing of compressors varies with type and duty but particular attention should be paid to the withdrawal of engine and compressor pistons, cam and crank shafts and oil cooler bundles and to the maintenance of cylinder valves, without obstruction from piping and supports.

Discharge piping on reciprocating compressors and sometimes on the suction piping is supplied with pulsation dampers which should be located as close to the compressor nozzles as possible. Air intakes should be provided with filters and located outside the compressor house preferably, well above grade and where the air is clean and cool. The intake piping should be kept as short and straight as possible, ideally falling vertically through the compressor house roof with the silencers above roof level.

Centrifugal   Centrifugal compressors often have complicated ancilliaries. They should be installed to facilitate dismantling and reassembly. Turnround time is reduced by using bottom suction and discharge connections. To achieve this the compressor is erected on a concrete plinth sufficiently above grade to accommodate pipe bends. The top cover can then be removed to expose the internals with the minimum of pipe removal.

General   There should be a clear space of about one half the width of a compressor (subject to a 1.5m minimum) between compressors, between rows of compressors and at the end of each row subject to any special maintenance considerations, (see *Figure 25*).

Compressors are generally provided with a degree of shelter which

Figure 25   *Compressor layout (by courtesy of Nuovo Pignone.)*

must be well ventilated to allow for the escape of flammable gas leaking from the machine.

Trenches, pits and similar gas traps should be avoided within gas compressor houses.

It is advisable to provide lifting facilities in the compressor house for maintenance purposes.

1.5.3 Fans

The inlet and outlet ducting local to a large fan (say $700sm^3/min$) must be kept in mind because of its large size, together with the space required for bends and the clearance around valves and filters (see *Figure 26*). Tight bends or fittings on ducting near the fan should be avoided because of their harmful effect on air flow. Fans may be housed in a separate building to isolate any noise problem and provide access under cover for operation and maintenance. Adequate space and headroom must be allowed for removal of impellers, shafts, motors, etc., particularly for dirty or corrosive duties. Generous foundation masses may be needed to damp out any vibrations and the fans should be located away from any external source of vibration.

Figure 26 *Fans on a gas reformer plant (by courtesy of Sturtevant Engineering Company.)*

1.6 Filters

Fot the more complicated types of filters the layout may with advantage be discussed with the manufacturer.

Line Filters and Strainers These are filters designed to remove only small amounts of solids. There should be access to take the element out for cleaning. Filters which have to be serviced more frequently than once a week should be accessible from the operating floor or platform. At lower service frequencies a fixed ladder may be sufficient.

Batch Filters This type of filter is usually operated under pressure, examples are plate and frame filters, leaf filters, and bed filters. They are usually housed in a building. They remove considerable quantities of solid which build up on the filter cloth or other filter medium as a cake which is periodically removed, possibly after washing. Consequently such filters are piped up in parallel so that some are filtering and some are washing whilst others are being decaked. Access to the changeover valves, pressure gauges, sight glasses and sample points is needed.

In filters that have to be opened for cake removal, layout is extremely important for ease of operation, but less so where decaking is done by air blowing or some other non-manual method, in which maintenance considerations may determine layout. A space of at least one filter's width should be left around the filter and if trolleys are used for bringing up new cloths, removal of the cake or transporting the filter plates, etc., the free space should be at least 1.75m. on one side. These types of filter are sometimes staggered at 45° thus saving space and effort by facilitating handling of trolleys since 90° turns are avoided.

To aid discharge the filter may be elevated but generally it is placed on a main floor discharging to the level below, Chutes must be of generous dimensions and as near vertical as possible.

Special ventilation (vapour hoods, spray nozzles and extractor fans) may be needed if the liquids are toxic or inflammable, but this should not interfere with the decaking of the filters. The floor should be designed so that it can be washed down and drained.

For larger filters having heavy internals such as plates, overhead lifting beams may be needed. A room may be required for storing cloths or filter media and for cutting filter cloths.

Continuous Filters   Typical of this class is the rotary vacuum filter (see *Figure 27*). If the slurry or cake is not adversely affected by the weather it may be placed in the open, with or without a shelter.

It is usually easier to transport and store slurries rather than filter cake, (i.e. pumps, pipework and storage tanks are generally to be preferred to conveyors and bunkers) and so normally the liquid/solid separation equipment should be located near the final solids discharge point. It is better to have one pump delivering to a feed vessel and a separate filter pump rather than utilising a single pump for transporting the slurry over a long distance and feeding the filter. Both pumps should have controls near the filter. The feed lines should be installed to prevent settlement and should have adequate drain and flushing points.

It is desirable that the filter should be located above the feed vessel. This allows the filter drains and overflow to be returned to the feed

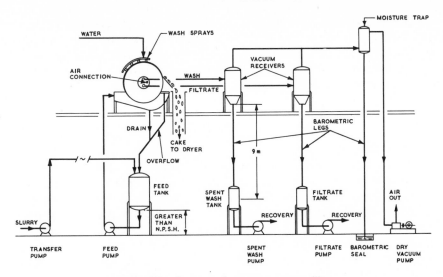

Figure 27 *Layout of rotary vacuum filter*

tank by gravity. The overflow should be vertical and of large diameter, desirably having facilities for rodding out and cleaning of any tees and bends which may be used. Isolating valves should be fitted direct on the trough at the drain connections so as to give a minimum pocket where solids can settle out. The valves should be accessible for operation but if necessary they are fitted with extended spindles or chain wheels.

An elevated filter simplifies the discharge of solids. Discharge chutes should be wide and steep to avoid blockage.

If the same pump is used both as a vacuum pump and as the filtrate pump then it is a liquid sealed type and it can be installed either on the same level as the filter or alongside the filtrate pump. Installation, close to the filter will tend to shorten the vacuum line. The air and water discharge lines from the pump should be arranged to the pump manufacturers' recommendations; otherwise a noisy air discharge through the water drain, or water discharge through the air silencer, may result.

Where the vacuum and filtrate pumps are separate a vacuum vessel is employed. This should be positioned near to the rotary valve, to keep the vacuum line short; the pipes should be arranged to give drainage by gravity. The filtrate receiver is at the bottom of the barometric leg underneath the vacuum vessel and acts as a seal tank so that the filtrate pump is not pumping from vacuum.

The filter should have good access(>1m) along the discharge side of the filter to facilitate the fitting of new filter cloths, etc. Access is required to the speed control unit on the drum drive, to the control valves near the rotary valve and for maintenance and lubrication. A lifting beam is not normally necessary.

1.7 Centrifuges

The layout should take account of the special characteristics of centrifuges which are expensive, high speed precision machines. The layout should always be discussed with manufacturers. If outdoor installation is being considered, ensure that adequate precautions have been taken against weather, condensation and low temperature. Machines should be mounted on a solid floor if possible with generous foundation masses to damp out vibrations, particularly when manually loaded batch units are used. The discharge of solids may require elevated installations. The manufacturer should be consulted to ensure that dynamic forces generated by the machine are known and can be absorbed by the foundation or structure.

The equipment should have a minimum of 1.5m access around each machine. Lifting beams should be provided for maintenance, and multiple machines are normally laid out in lines to minimise the number of beams. Piping around the machine should not impinge on the space for the withdrawal of motors, bowls etc.

Centrifuges should be installed away from external sources of vibration. Centrifuges should not be under corrosive areas or piping since spillages can corrode safety interlocks, motors, control wiring etc. Spillage and leakage should be contained in a curbed area provided with a fall to a gully connected to the plant effluent system.

The problems of feeding and of cake discharge from centrifuges are similar to those of filters (see Part II Section 1.6). However as centrifuges can discharge large volumes of air a vent may have to be fitted to the hopper. This should be carried outside the building if the fumes are noxious.

1.8 Dryers and Similar Gas-Solid Contactors

For the purpose of layout dryers can be classified as follows:

1) Vessel shaped (spray, fluidised bed)
2) Conveyor (pneumatic, screw conveyor, perforated belt conveyor)

3) Tray (batch and continuous)
4) Rotary (internal and drum)

A large drier (e.g. kilns up to 230m long × 7.5m diameter for cement, lime or other calcination process) is often weatherproofed and placed in the open to save building costs with just the filter bags and instrumentation housed in a small building.

Where there is a dust explosion risk the dryer is separated from the other items and fitted with explosion reliefs (see *Figure 28*). The direction of the reliefs should be away from other plants, buildings or roads and must be taken through the roof for dryers in buildings.

On the gas exit stream of dryers, with direct contact between the gases and solids, there are cyclones or some form of dust removal (see Part II Section 1.11).

If buildings are used their size and layout is determined by the access required for erection and maintenance, with due consideration to the feed and product flow arrangements. Within the building dust collecting surfaces should be avoided, because of the risk of explosion.

The air heater on smaller installations is a steam air exchanger (see Part II Section 1.4). It can be housed outside the building. Larger installations have oil or gas fired heaters, either direct or indirect. They may be integral with the drier. They can be considered as furnaces (see Part II Section 1.2).

Sufficient elevation is needed in vessel and rotary driers to enable the product to fall by gravity to the product conveyor.

Vessel Shaped Dryers The considerations of Part II Section 1.1 on reactors and mixers apply and the feeding of slurries to spray driers follows the practice indicated in the section on filters (Part II Section 1.6). In sizing the building at least 2m clearance over and around the dryer should be left plus any additional room for the withdrawal of internals.

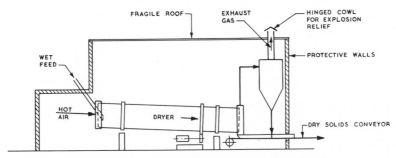

Figure 28   *Rotary cylinder dryer explosion chamber*

Figure 29 *Anhydro spray dryer in anhydro laboratory (by courtesy of APV Company Ltd.)*

For spray dryers, as a general guide, the operating platform and dryer support should be at one half the building height unless this interferes with the discharge. Consideration should be given to using a flat bottomed unit as this reduces the height needed in a building.

Conveyor Dryers The section on conveyors (Part II Section 1.12). applies with allowance for insulation and thermal expansion. (see *Figure 30*).

Tray Dryers In using tray dryers a number of operations can be identified (see *Figure 31*). Tray drying is a production line operation like packaging and filling (see Part II Section 2.4).

If operation is manual then layout design is principally an ergonom-

Figure 30 *Pneumatic conveyor dryer with cyclone (by courtesy of APV Company Ltd.)*

ic problem. For example trays should be filled and emptied on tables and the trollies suitably designed so that trays can easily be handled. If the operation is automated then the type of drier and the method of transporting the solids determines the layout, and the equipment manufacturer should be consulted. For both systems there should be areas for cleaning and storage of trays and trollies. This prevents the working areas being cluttered with spare trays etc.

The drying area may have to be ventilated and de-traying booths used if the powders are toxic, etc. Cross contamination of products may be avoided by partitioning off the drying area.

Rotary Dryers   Rotary dryers with exposed moving parts have to

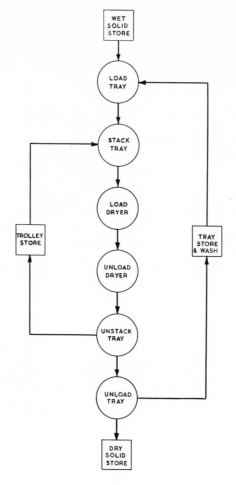

Figure 31   *Operations in tray drying*

be guarded. This is usually done by the manufacturer, but also the lay-out engineer should arrange his design so that operators are kept away from the moving drum.

After-Coolers   In large driers it is often necessary to cool the product when natural heat losses are insufficient. Pneumatic, rotary or vibratory conveyor coolers may be used. Similarly considerations as for driers apply to the layout of after-coolers.

References   See References 21–25 on Explosion Relief.

1.9 Mills and Crushers

Equipment manufacturers must be consulted as to type and size of machine to be used. A very wide range can be offered to suit physical properties of material, size of feed and product, capacity, etc. Each type of mill or crusher is suited for a particular application. They are made in various sizes to suit a wide range of capacities from 2Mg to 2000Mg per hour, and may be classified as follows:

Coarse Communication—Product down to 30 mesh
1) Gyratory or cone crushers
2) Jaw crushers
3) Roll crusher

Fine Comminution—Product down to 350 mesh from approx 50 mesh feed
1) Ball mills
2) Rod mills
3) Hammer mills
4) Impact breakers
5) Attrition pulverisers

Superfine Comminution—Product below 350 mesh
1) Vibration mills
2) Fluid energy mills

When dry grinding is recommended, the dust problems must be examined, and precautions must be taken, to minimise air pollution and avoid explosions (see *References 21–25*). This may involve the use of filters, cyclones, protective buildings, explosion relief etc. which could require at least as much space as the milling equipment they serve.

Multiple items, are usually arranged in line, to simplify the feeding and delivery systems. The feed arrangement is of prime importance in order to obtain maximum efficiency—attention being paid to the makers requirements. It should be either in the direction of rotation of the mill, or vertical and at a controlled rate by conveyor of mechanical feeder.

The machines and their drives are usually housed in a building, adjacent to an access road and supported at grade on concrete foundations. It is unwise to elevate the larger machines due to excessive vibration, but if this must be done, great care should be taken to eliminate or reduce the vibration by adequately bracing the supporting platforms. Lift beams must be provided over the machines for maintenance purposes (see *Figure 32*).

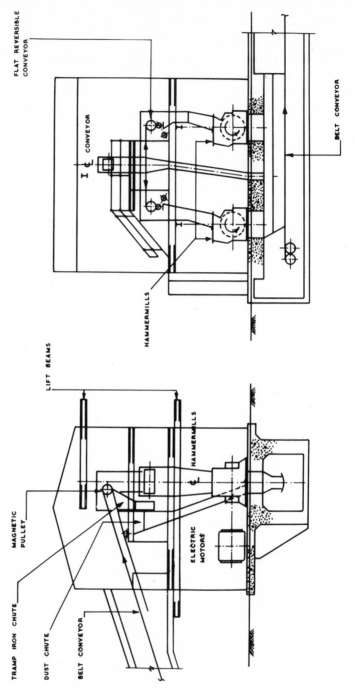

Figure 32   *Typical layout in hammer-mill house*

The access around a crusher or mill can be taken as approximately the width of the machine, particular consideration being given to access to breaker plate adjustment screws, tramp iron boxes, inspection doors, removal of rods, etc.

The machine suppliers will specify the drive horsepower requirements and recommend whether drive should be direct through a flexible or fluid coupling, vee-rope or belt, or spur gear reducer.

As a precaution to avoid damage to the machine, it may be advisable to install a magnet in the stream to extract tramp iron. *Figure 33* illustrates an electro-magnetic suspended over the conveyor. The magnetic is moved to one side along the runway beam to discharge the tramp iron to a hopper or trolley. *Figure 34* shows a magnetic head pulley which automatically discharges the iron to a chute.

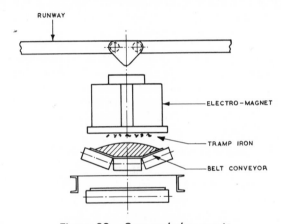

Figure 33   *Suspended magnet*

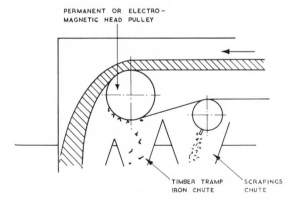

Figure 34   *Magnetic pulley*

1.10 Screens

Screening can generally be divided into two classifications:

1) Sizing, which is the separation of particles into a number of fractions.

2) Scalping, which involves the simpler operation of splitting the material into two fractions such as removing the underside fraction before crushing, or the final removal of dust or unwanted fines that have occurred in storage or handling since the sizing process.

Vibrating screens are invariably used for size control in association with crushing and grinding of dry material. Sizes vary considerably and it is important that each installation is carefully laid out, ensuring that minimum angles of feed and delivery chutes are used. Vibrating screens may slope from horizontal to 25° and have one, two or three screening decks.

'Grizzlies' are used primarily for scalping or making a high capacity primary separation. Two types are used, the 'fixed bar' type and the 'live roll' type. There are no problems involved in the layout or 'grizzlies', the size being dependent on the throughput, and the incline to suit the material. For layout purposes 'fixed-bar' screens should be inclined at 45° and 'live-roll' at 20°.

It is usually desirable to place a screen above the equipment or silos into which it feeds. A screen takes feed from one stream of material and splits it into a number of streams. By elevating the screen, one stream only is to be elevated whilst the fractions fall by gravity through chutes or into hoppers (see *Figure 35*).

Screens may be supported either by suspension, from the floor below, or a combination of both. Totally enclosed screens should be used when necessary to minimise a possible dust nuisance. Space must always be allowed above a screen for maintaining and replacement of screen cloths, and for the larger units, a lifting beam should be installed to facilitate this.

In laying out screening and associated equipment, it is imperative to layout the hoppers and chutes first, since these will dictate the relative elevation of the equipment. Furthermore, since belt conveyors are generally associated with screens and grinding equipment, the maximum elevation of the equipment will determine the distance between the various sections, and the overall size of the plant. For each additional metre in elevation, a belt conveyor needs to be increased by approximately three metres in length, so it can be seen how important it is to determine elevations in this kind of layout.

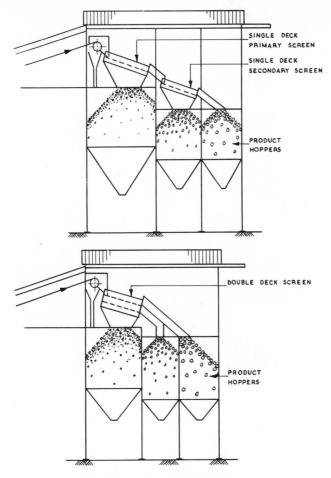

Figure 35   *Sizing examples*

1.11 Cyclones, Air Filters and Precipitators

Dust removers and collectors are fitted to driers, crushers, conveyors, stacks, etc. They can vary in size and complexity from a simple cyclone to a large electrostatic precipitator used in cement production. A main concern of layout is free flow of the recovered solids.

Cyclones are usually light and can be laid out in any convenient position which allows free flow of the recovered solids. An air seal has to be provided at the solids discharge. If a bag filter (see *Figure 36*) or a wet filter is used, access should be provided for element replacement.

Figure 36   *Bag filter installation (by courtesy of W. C. Holmes & Co. Ltd.)*

Figure 37   *Electrostatic precipitators (by courtesy of W. C. Holmes & Co. Ltd.)*

Some electrostatic precipitators are outwardly large boxes with collector hoppers underneath that discharge the fine dust (see *Figure 37*). Layout problems are associated with their large physical size and with suitably arranging the ducting from the drier or kilns to the precipitator, from the precipitator to the fan or fans, and then to the stack.

As for driers (Part II Section 1.8) there can be an explosion hazard in which case dust removers should be housed in a special building and their ducting fitted with explosion relief doors, etc., (see *References 21–25* and *26*).

Reference   See Reference 26 on Explosions in Cyclones.

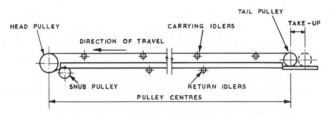

Figure 38   *Typical troughed belt conveyor*

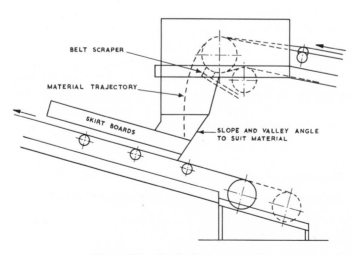

Figure 39   *Typical chute detail*

1.12 Conveyors

1.12.1 Mechanical

The most common mechanical means of conveying loose bulk materials is the troughed belt conveyor (*Figures 38* and *39*). Belt conveyors have a certain minimum distance that they can be located from the units due to the maximum angle of slope of the conveyor, generally inclined to angles up to 20° and declined to 15°. Usually fine granular materials can be conveyed at steeper angles than course or lumpy materials. Belt widths range from 0.3m–1.8m.

Draglink or Redler conveyors can be set at much steeper angles, even vertically in some cases, so that minimum spacing here is much less. This type of conveyor is only suitable for certain friable, granular materials and should be specified only after prior consultation with the manufacturers who may consider making tests. Bucket elevators are vertical and allow the store to be adjacent to the unit feeding place or being fed. However they require more maintenance than other types. Combination of horizontal conveyors and bucket elevators gives maximum flexibility regarding store to plant spacing.

For multiple belt conveyors a maintenance walkway, 600mm minimum, must be provided alongside each conveyor. Two conveyors arranged in parallel can have a single walkway of 750mm between each of them. The walkway level should be approximately 750mm below the belt line. When conveyors link process buildings or store at an elevated level, supporting gantries are provided. These may be enclosed or open dependent on the materials being conveyed (*Figure 40*).

Allowance must be made in the layout for tensioning the belt (*Figure 38*). This is usually done with a tension screw at the tail end of the conveyor for belts up to 60m long. For longer conveyors an automatic gravity weight method is used. This may be positioned at any convenient point on the return strand of the conveyor (when the take up is vertical), or at the tail end (when the take up is horizontal like the screw). The amount of tensioning required can be taken as 2% of the distance between the pulley centres.

1.12.2 Pneumatic

Two types of pneumatic conveyor are commonly used:

1) Air assisted gravity conveying (fluidising)
2) Pressure conveying

Fluidised conveyors are continuous, near horizontal air conveyors

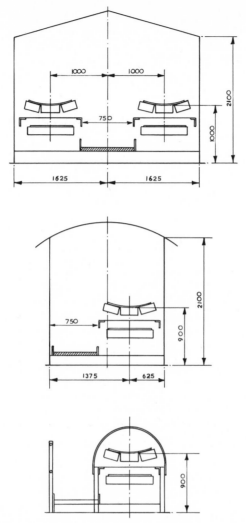

Figure 40 *Typical supporting gantries for 750mm wide belt conveyors*

used for fluidising a powder and conveying it speedily to a lower level. The angle of slope for fluidised conveyors (*Figure 41*) is dependent on many design factors but may be taken as 5° for layout purposes. A fluidised conveyor may 'snake' in plan, and have 'take-off' points at any position along its length.

In pressure conveying the material is carried along in the air. Operation and maintenance access should be provided around the

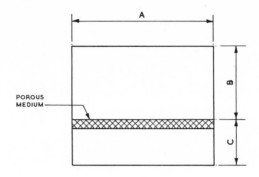

Dimensions for powder with density 1000 kg/m³			
A mm	B mm	C mm	APPROX. CAPACITY m³/hr.
100	100	50	8·5
150	100	50	17·0
200	150	75	28·0
250	150	75	56·0
300	200	75	74·0
350	250	75	112·0
400	250	75	224·0

Figure 41   *Typical cross section through a fluidised gravity conveyor*

blowing unit and at the separation zone (collector and filter unit), (see Part II Section 1.11). The layout details of the conveyor tube (such as the minimum radii of bends to prevent blockage) should be settled in consultation with the manufacturers.

Care must be taken to site the air intake to give a clean supply. If the air is prefiltered, access is needed to service the air filter (see Part II section 1.11).

References See Reference 76 on Trough Belt Conveyors, and Reference 52 on Pneumatic Conveying.

Figure 42   *Inert gas generators (by courtesy of W. C. Holmes Ltd.)*

1.13 Specialised and Packaged Plants

A number of plants may be bought as comlete packages and the user has to provide suitable space for the package. Typical of these are service plants such as water treatment, inert gas (see *Figure 42*), refrigeration, boiler, and cryogenic plants. Process plants for producing acids or for various kinds of recovery are also sold as packages. Electrochemical plant such as chlorine producing equipment (see *References 15* and *16* or a reducing plant (see *Figure 43*) is provided as a package.

Figure 43   *Cell house for reductive dimerisation of acrylonitrile (by courtesy of Monsanto Company.)*

The layout within such packages, incorporates the results of experience by the vendor and commonly is more compact than normal plant. Although the layout offered may not be the optimum for a particular situation it is usually best to accept the layout as non-standard layouts cost extra.

There are a number of specialised plants peculiar to a particular industry and their layout is accomplished by referring to internal company guides. Examples of this are spinning machines in the synthetic fibres industry and the need on nuclear installations. (see *References 54* and *55*) to place plants behind biological shields.

Finally a plant may have a single specialised item amongst otherwise more usual items, for example, a tabletting machine. A combination of general layout principles and consultation with the manufacturers will achieve good layout in these cases.

References   See References 15 and 16 on Electrochemical Plant Layout, References 54 and 55 on Radioactive Plant Layout, and Reference 9 on Cryogenic Plant Layout.

2 LAYOUT OF STORAGE

2.1 Liquid Storage

Tank farms should preferably be placed on one side or not more than two sides of the process plant area. This arrangement allows adequate safety precautions to be taken and gives the possibility to expand either the tank farm area or process plant areas at any time in the future. Access must be allowed on all four sides of each tank bund area, and all roads should be linked in such a way that access is always possible should any road be cut by fire (see *Figure 44*).

Loading gantries can be located on any external side of the tank farm except the process plant side. They should preferably be as far away from the process plant as process considerations will allow, since they are sources of accidents. However, a compromise will have to be made in locating the loading gantries, when considering the location of the pumping station and the length of the suction lines to the gantries.

For liquid loading and unloading by road the area required will be made up of the area for actual platform and equipment plus the area for standing of the tankers. As an example, for a loading island with, say, 2–3 loading arms, allow an area 7.5m × 1.8m with 3m each side of the island for standing of vehicles. Separate inlet and outlet routes should be provided and bottlenecks should not result through long

Figure 44   *Typical tank farm layout (by courtesy of Esso Petroleum Company Ltd.)*

standing or breakdown of tankers. A table of approximate main dimensions of typical road tankers and fuel carriers with turning circles is in the *Tables 4* and *5*. For loading by rail see *Reference 74*.

The spacing of tanks from other equipment depends on the class of liquid according to their flash points. Class A products have flash points below 23°C. Class B flash points between 23 and 66°C inclusive and Class C a flash point above 66°C. Typical spacings are given in *Table 6*. Note that if class C liquids are stored at temperatures above the flash point they must be treated as Class A or B.

For certain liquids either burial or sunshields are either necessary or desirable. Cooling facilities may be required on occasion. In all cases layout will have to satisfy local authorities for fire regulations, safety and access. Tanks containing flammable liquids should be bunded or diked except those containing fluids with a high flash point at storage temperature (e.g. Class C, asphalt, heavy fuel oils, etc.). In this case a low wall 450mm high may be desirable in order to control spillage and prevent pollution.

Areas around tanks can be varied in both shape and size to suit land available. The type of bund wall or dike can be varied. In cases where space is available 'earth' types with side slopes of $1\frac{1}{2}$–2 horizontal to 1 vertical are cheapest but as they are less than $1\frac{1}{2}$m high they require more space. Where space is at a premium concrete or masonry construction is advantageous. A desirable maximum height for safe access is 2.4m but this may be exceeded for very large tanks. Steps should be provided over the bund with additional emergency exits as required. The minimum effective capacity within the retaining wall should be equal to 110% that of the largest tank. This rate is based on the assumption that only one tank will fail at a time.

Tanks should be grouped and bunded so that the contents of the tanks in one bund will require one type of fire-fighting equipment only. This applies particularly when both water miscible and water immiscible liquids are stored in the same installation. Space should be allowed for foam or drenching systems. For tanks grouped together consideration should be given to a common walkway with not less than two means of escape, dependent upon the number of tanks served. Tanks larger then 18m diameter should be accessible from roads on two sides of the tank. The total capacity of fixed roof tanks in any one bund should not exceed 60,000m³ irrespective of the products contained. For floating roof tanks the maximum capacity is 120,000m³ except for individual tanks which may have greater capacities. The maximum number of tanks in one bund should not exceed 6 when

Table 4 *Details for rigid chassis road tankers*

Make	Type	Turning Circle Dia. m	Overall Length m	Overall width m	Overall Height (Laden) m
A.E.C. Mercury	6½m³ Lub Oil T.T.	17.0	7.2	2.23	2.67
Albion Caledonian	15m³ Fuel Oil T.T.	20.7	9.1	2.28	2.84
Austin	5Mg Package Truck	16.4	6.6	2.28	2.97
Bedford	7Mg Open Tail Gate	16.7	6.9	2.13	2.97
Bedford	8m³ Spirit T.T.	16.7	6.8	2.13	2.69
Bedford	6½m³ Fuel Oil T.T.	16.7	7.1	2.28	2.38
Ford	8m³ Spirit T.T.	16.1	7.1	2.28	2.51
Ford	7m³ Spirit T.T.	16.1	7.3	2.28	2.59
Leyland Octopus	18m³ Spirit T.T.	21.0	9.1	2.36	2.94
Leyland	15m³ Fuel T.T.	21.0	9.1	2.44	2.89
Leyland	13m³ Transformer	21.0	9.1	2.28	2.89
Scammell	15m³ Fuel Oil T.T.	22.8	9.1	2.28	3.33

Table 5   *Details for articulated road tankers*

Make	Type	Turning Circle Dia. m	Overall m	Overall Width m	Overall Height (Laden) m
AEC Mandator	18m³ Spirit T.T.	14.3	10.2	2.28	2.99
Bedford Carrimore	9m³ Spirit T.T.	11.5	8.3	2.26	2.51
Bedford Carrimore	11m³ Spirit T.T.	11.5	9.0	2.28	2.46
Bedford Carrimore	6Mg Open Truck	10.3	9.4	2.20	2.08
Foden	18m³ Spirit T.T.	15.7	10.2	2.44	2.67
Foden	15m³ Spirit T.T.	15.7	10.0	2.41	3.35
Leyland Beaver	18m³ Spirit T.T.	14.3	10.2	2.28	2.79

Table 6   *Typical spacings for liquid storage vessels*

(Distance given is from the outside of vessel which contains a particular class of liquid to the edge of the reference item).

Class A/B liquids to site boundary, or other site buildings, processes etc.
    30m
Class C liquids to site boundary or other site building, process, etc.
    15m
All classes to pump house, filling shed, road and rail loading racks
    15m
All classes to bund
    0.5 × largest diameter subject to 15m maximum and 3m minimum distance
Between different groups of Class A/B in separate bunds
    30m
Between Class A/B and Class C groups in separate bunds
    7.5m
Between tanks of Class C in separate or common bunds
    As convenient
Between tanks within a Class A/B Group in common bunds
    See Notes (a) and (b) half diameter of biggest tank or 15m
whichever is the least
Between tanks of mixed A/B/C in common bund
    As A/B in common bund

Note (a)   For crude storage tanks the distance is 0.5 the largest tank diameter or 30m whichever is the greater
     (b)   The IP Code should be consulted as it can allow closer spacing for floating roof tanks (see *Reference 76*)

the total capacity exceeds 12,000m^3 for fixed roof (24,000m^3 for floating roof). Below these figures there is no limit on the number of tanks. Tanks of 30,000m^3 for fixed roof (60,000m^3 for floating roof) should be separately bunded.

When exothermic chemical reaction is possible between stored liquids, tanks should be segregated and not bunded together. Where polymerisation is probable, each tank shall be segregated from other tanks and consideration should be given to increasing the spacing as much as possible.

For an ungrouped tank which contains liquid with a boil-over tendency, the capacity within its oil retaining wall should be in general that of the tank itself. If, however, the tank concerned is equiped with a floating roof and if the space within the retaining wall is connected to an adequate oil disposal sewer the minimum capacity within the wall itself may be half that of the tank. Should an ungrouped tank contain a Class A or Class B product without boil-over the minimum capacity within the oil retaining wall should in general be equal to that of the tank. If, however, the space within the retaining wall is connected to an adequate disposal sewer the contained capacity must be reduced to half of that of the tank.

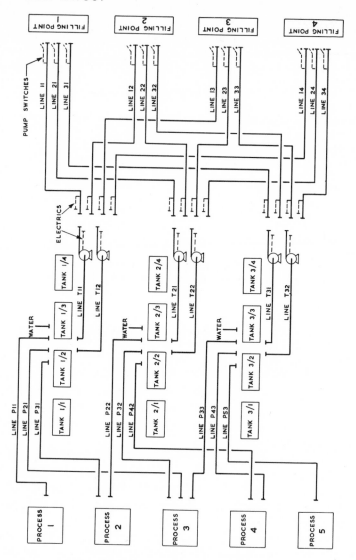

Figure 45   *Variable multi-storage layout*

It is not considered necessary that the area around atmospheric storage tanks containing dangerous liquids such as acids and caustic soda should be enclosed. This is providing that they do not spill onto road, gangways or working areas and that there can be no interaction between different fluids if two leak (e.g. acid and NaCN solution). In the latter cases the tanks should be separated by distance.

The layout of storage tanks and related facilities are affected by general pump arrangements. Pumps related to storage can be in groups or located individually to serve one or two tanks. Groups of pumps will facilitate centralised operation but may require long suction runs of piping and thus prove costly. Lines carrying hot or flammable materials should be as short as possible.

Pumps should not be located in bunded areas round flammable liquid storage. The vertical distance between tank outlet and pump suction elevations will be at least twice the anticipated tank settlement after initial loading. Steps should be provided where access routes cross pipework.

Where tanks are heated space must be left for withdrawal of coils.

Storage and tankage areas need not be provided with any lighting if it can be reasonably assumed that they will not be visited by operating personnel during the hours of darkness. In cases of emergency, operating personnel will have to carry portable lamps.

For smaller plants, storage tanks can be sited to suit the flow arrangement and be individually located but general principles already quoted regarding fire hazard, spillage, distances from other plant, access etc., should be followed.

For multiple product storage where the products vary according to seasonal or other changes in demand layout is important to prevent accidental mixing of two products and to permit flushing and cleaning of tanks and pipes. In these cases individual tanks should not be hard-piped to the production plants nor to the tanker or container filling points. A number of lines should be run from the production area to the storage area and from the storage area to the filling area and then connected up with flexible hose according to production requirements (see Part II Section 1.1.1 on batch reactors). A possible arrangement is given in *Figure 45*. The filling pumps whilst situated near the tanks should be controlled from the filling points.

References   See References 74 and 75 on Storage.

2.2 Gas and Pressure Storage

Many fluids used as gases require pressure storage. Products which are gases at normal atmospheric temperature and pressure are stored under moderate pressure and/or refrigeration. Such products can also be stored as liquids under pressure (e.g. Nitrogen). In view of the

Notes on Table 7

1) Measure in plan from the nearest point of the vessel, or from associated fittings from which an escape can occur when these are located away from the vessel.

2) If this distance cannot be achieved, the need for suitable fire protection of the cable or pipeline should be considered.

3) The tanks containing water soluble non-hydrocarbons being bunded, power cables and pipelines at ground level should be outside the bund and so protected by the bund from fire in the tanks.

4) Flammable liquids are those with flash points up to 66°C.

5) Measured in plan from the nearest part of the bund wall except where otherwise indicated.

6) The Home Office Code for Storage of LPG at Fixed installations recommends 45m for C_4 as well as C_3 storage, which is considered to be unnecessarily conservative. The designer may be able to persuade the Licencing Authority to lower this to 15m in view of the significant difference in rate of vaporisation of the respective materials. Irrespective of distance no ignition source should be in the bund.

7) A group of vessels should not exceed 10,000m³ unless a single vessel. Spacing between such groups should be a minimum of 15m between adjacent vessels. The bund to have a net volume not less than 100% of capacity of the largest tank in the bund, after deducting volume up to bund height of all other tanks in the same bund.

8) A group of tanks should not exceed 60,000m³. Spacing of the nearest tanks in any two such groups, which may have a common bund wall should be such that the tank in one group should be a minimum of 15m from the inside top of the bund of any adjacent group(s).

nature of these products, special safety precautions should be observed in the layout of such vessels. Minimum recommendations are indicated in *Table 7*.

For the storage of non-flammable gases at pressure, there is no restriction on the spacing within a group but a group should be a distance of 15m from any other group or equipment. Similar considerations to these apply for low pressure gas holders for all gases.

References   See References 27–32 on Gas Pressure Storage.

2.3 Bulk Solids Storage

The layout of bulk solids storage will depend mainly upon the type of storage, and the method adopted for loading and unloading the material.

The main types of storage systems are:

1) Open pile for materials unaffected by weather

2) Closed warehouses

3) Vertical silos

Table 7 *Liquid flammable gases: safety distances for location and spacing*

Minimum Distance	Material Stored		
	Hydrocarbons	Non-Hdyrocarbons insoluble in water	Non-Hydrocarbons soluble in water
Pressure Storage (1)(7)			
To boundary, process units, buildings containing a source of ignition, or any other fixed sources of ignition.	Ethylene 60m C₃'s 45m C₄'s 30m	Methyl Chloride 23m Vinyl Chloride 23m Methyl Vinyl Ether 23m Ethyl Chloride 15m	Methylamines 15m
To building containing flammable materials, e.g. filling shed.	15m	15m	15m
To road or rail tank wagon filling points	15m	15m	15m
To overhead power lines and pipe bridges	15m	15m	15m
To other above ground power cables and important pipelines or pipelines likely to increase the hazard.	(2) 7.5m	(2) 7.5m	See Note (3) less than 15m for 750m³ but not less than 1.8m for ≤50m³ or
Between pressure storage vessels	One quarter of sum of diameters of adjacent tanks but not less than		
To low pressure refrigerated tanks	15m from the bund wall of the low pressure tank, but not less than 30m from the low pressure tank shell.		
To flammable liquid (4) storage tanks	15m from the bund wall of the flammable liquid tank.		
Low Pressure Refrigerated Storage (5)(8)			
To boundary, process units, buildings containing a source of ignition, or any other fixed sources of ignition. (6)	Ethylene 90m C₃'s 45m C₄'s 15m		Ethylene Oxide 15m
To building containing flammable materials, e.g. filling shed.	15m		15m
To road or rail tanker filling point	15m		15m
To overhead power lines and pipebridges	15m		15m
Between low pressure refrigerated tank shells	One half of sum of diameters of adjacent tanks		
To flammable liquid (4) storage tanks	Not less than 30m between low pressure refrigerated LFG and flammable liquid tank shells, but LFG and flammable liquids must be in separate bunds.		
To pressure storage vessels	As defined above under Pressure Storage.		

Open Piles   Many variations of large open pile systems are available, all with different types of stocking out and reclaiming methods. It is the cheapest way of storing bulk materials, but usually because of dust etc. has to be located in a good open space away from the main usage point.

The simplest way to load a pile is to discharge material from a dump truck near the storage area, then use a front-end loader to move it into a neat pile. Reclaiming is carried out by a front-end loader which dumps the material into the feed hopper of a bucket elevator, conveyor, or possibly directly into equipment. In plan this type of storage requires an area equivalent to the largest pile required, plus space left around it for manoevering the loading trucks and mechanical equipment. The space allocated will be connected to the unloading apron and to the road network coming from the material source.

A more sophisticated type of open pile is fed by a belt conveyor placed above the storage area at the maximum angle of inclination allowed by the material being handled (see *Figure 46*). This is dependent on the angle of repose of the material and the inclination of the conveyor which may be up to 20°. The pile will be conical. The system is not suitable for friable materials due to the dropping height. This can be partially overcome by making the top section of the feeding coveyor hinged.

For larger capacity open stock piles, a Drag-Scraper system may be used (see *Figure 47*). A head-post is placed near to the centre of the store with the discharge point below it. A travelling tail car on rails is connected to the head post by a cable system carrying a scraper bucket. Material is reclaimed by dragging the scraper over the top of the pile and discharging into an underground hopper in front of the

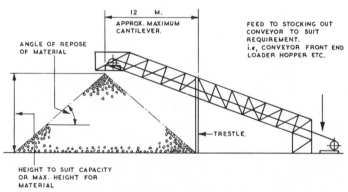

Figure 46   *Single conical open stockpile fed by belt conveyor*

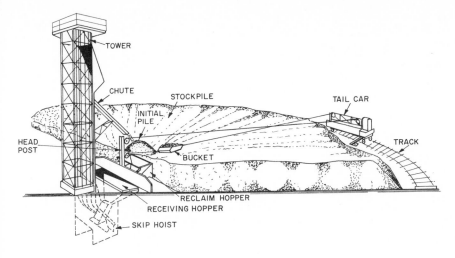

Figure 47   *Typical drag scraper scheme*

head-post. Loading the pile can be accomplished by means of an elevated belt conveyor or skip hoist to form an initial pile or an overhead cable car system. The initial pile is then spread to the required point in the store by using the scraper bucket.

Another method for storing materials in the open is by means of an elevated belt conveyor with a travelling tripper carriage (see *Figure 48*). This will form rectangular shape stockpiles of any length. Reclaiming again can be by use of front end loaders or other proprietary makes of reclaiming machines, i.e. bucket wheel reclaimers.

Closed Warehouses   Where conditions do not allow open piling of material, closed warehouses can be used. These are usually rectangular in plan, but may be circular (see *Figure 49*).

Loading of a closed store is generally by an overhead belt conveyor which in turn is fed by an elevator or another inclined belt conveyor. Piles are reclaimed by front end loaders discharging on to belt conveyors running along the side of the warehouse or by underground conveyors loaded through openings in the floor. Other types of reclaiming machines are available that will scrape the material from the side of the pile and into an underground conveyor.

For layout purposes, the warehouse should be positioned first and the feed and discharge conveyors can be placed at any convenient angle in plan, to and from the warehouse. Access must be provided at both ends of the building to facilitate movement of equipment.

Warehouses may be used to store different materials, or grades of

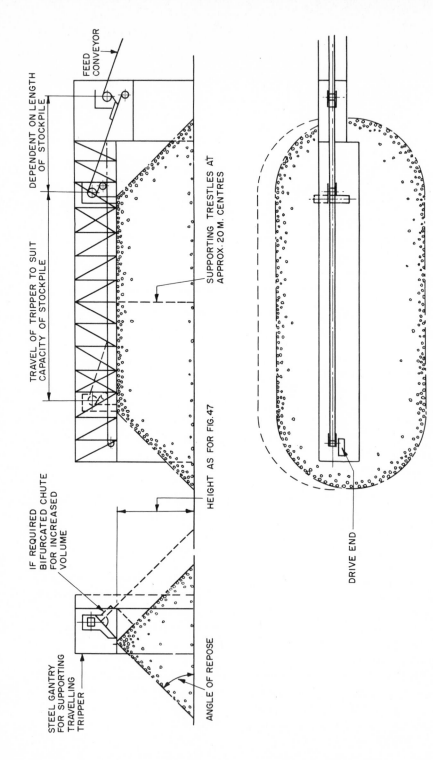

FEED CONVEYOR

DEPENDENT ON LENGTH OF STOCKPILE

TRAVEL OF TRIPPER TO SUIT CAPACITY OF STOCKPILE

SUPPORTING TRESTLES AT APPROX. 20 M. CENTRES

IF REQUIRED BIFURCATED CHUTE FOR INCREASED VOLUME

HEIGHT AS FOR FIG. 47

STEEL GANTRY FOR SUPPORTING TRAVELLING TRIPPER

ANGLE OF REPOSE

DRIVE END

Figure 48   Large open stockpile fed by travelling tripper conveyor

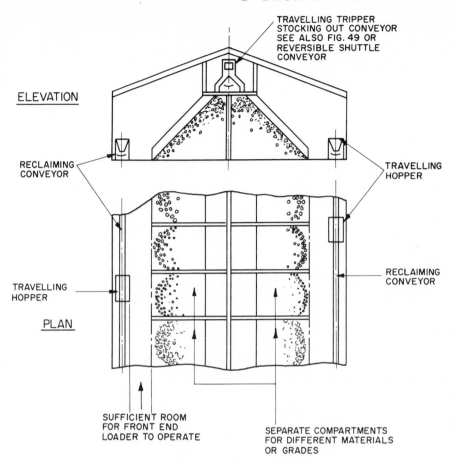

ELEVATION

TRAVELLING TRIPPER
STOCKING OUT CONVEYOR
SEE ALSO FIG. 49 OR
REVERSIBLE SHUTTLE
CONVEYOR

RECLAIMING
CONVEYOR

TRAVELLING
HOPPER

TRAVELLING
HOPPER

RECLAIMING
CONVEYOR

PLAN

SUFFICIENT ROOM
FOR FRONT END
LOADER TO OPERATE

SEPARATE COMPARTMENTS
FOR DIFFERENT MATERIALS
OR GRADES

Figure 49   *Warehouse-type materials store*

one material, by dividing with partition walls across the width. In certain cases there may be several separate warehouses grouped together, one for each type of material and internally divided according to various grades of each material.

Vertical Silos   With smaller quantities of materials vertical silos are the best choice (see *Figure 41*). They have a great advantage in keeping the material in a closed space that is not affected by wind or contamination. If the material is free flowing, they can be very easily discharged by gravity, but normally some mechanical assistance is required. This includes the use of vibratory feeders, rotary valves, rotary table dischargers, or screw conveyors to aid, control and meter

Table 8 Open pile storage

1. The height of a right conical pile is given by:

$$h = \sqrt[3]{\frac{3V.\tan^2\theta}{\pi}}$$

Where h = height of cone (m)
V = volume (m³)
θ = angle of repose of material

Assuming a conveyor angle of 18°, the "plan length" of the conveyor is:

$L_1 = 3.08h$ L_1 = horizontal conveyor length (m)

The radius of the bottom of the pile is: $r = h/\tan\theta$, where r = pile radius
or $r = h.\cot.\theta$

It follows that the minimum space required for a conveyor and pile in one straight line on plan is, $L_2 = L_1 + r$ or,

$$L_2 = (3.08 + \cot.\theta)\left(\sqrt[3]{\frac{3V.\tan^2\theta}{\pi}}\right)$$

2. Approximate volume of straight conical pile where the angle of repose is 37°,

$V = 1.327\ h^2.L_3 + 1.845\ h^3$ where L_3 is centre to centre distance of pile (m)

3. Approximate volume of circular pile where the angle of repose is 37°,

$V = (0.0232\ h^2.R + 1.845\ h^2)$ per degree circular arc   where R = radius of circular arc (m)

Table 9   *Approximate space requirements for closed warehouses*

NOTE: This table may be used to estimate space requirements for closed warehouses. It assumes a storage having an angle of repose of 37° fully triangular cross section and no spaces around the pile for conveyors or mechanical unloading equipment. Use table as it is for underground conveyor. In the case of unloading from one side, add 5m. to the width of the store. Add 10%–20% to length to account for dead spaces. B.D. = bulk density.

m Pile Height	m Width Base	Volume m Per Meter Length	Mg/m B.D. = 1	Mg/m B.D. = 1.5	Mg/m B.D. = 2	m Length Per Gg B.D. = 1
5	13.3	33	33	50	66	30.3
10	26.6	133	133	200	266	7.5
20	39.9	300	300	450	600	3.3
20	53.2	532	532	800	1064	1.9

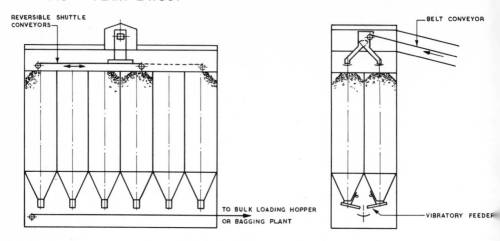

Figure 50   *Typical layout of vertical silos*

the discharge. For more difficult materials, bin activators or fluidisation may be used.

Silos can be round or square in cross-section. Loading of silos is carried out in the same way as warehouses, by bucket elevator, Redler, belt conveyor or pneumatically.

2.4 Filling and Packaging Equipment.

Filling and packaging operations are carried out on arrangements varying from simple belts with manual operations to highly mechanised automated installations. *Figure 51* shows the operations on a typical packaging line.

In order to achieve a balanced flow of containers and materials, use of local stores should be considered. A supply route direct from main stores can result in either line stoppages while awaiting components, or excess of materials stored local to the packaging line. Local stores should be positioned near to but not at the packaging line site with movement by conveyor, chute or truck. Visual contact between local stores and line supervision is advantageous. If local stores are not possible then adequate area must be allowed local to the packaging line for buffer storage of components with adequate access from supply routes.

Scale and type of equipment will be dictated by style of package and optimum production rate. The optimum production rate will arise

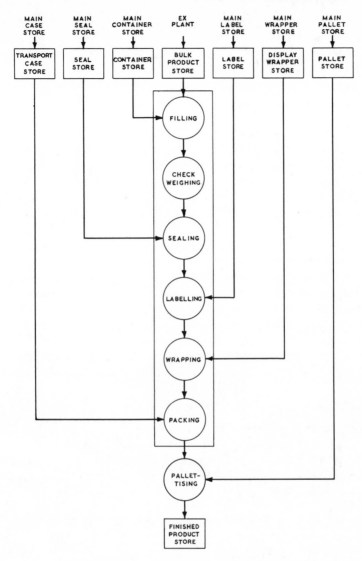

Figure 51   *Packaging and filling line*

from a variety of factors; batch size, hence packaging quantity, finished stock investment, capital cost, labour requirement. Transfer operations between individual machines must be carefully examined to minimise line losses. On automated lines, use of buffering systems such as rotary or moving belt tables should be considered between machines so that line operation can continue if one machine is out of service. In industries such as detergents, foods, etc., single product and container conditions with large volume give rise to high speed highly mechanised systems (200 per minute and upwards), whereas in pharmaceutical, cosmetics, etc., speeds are low (20–100 per minute). In the latter case use is made of a single line for different pack sizes of one product or one product group and hence ease of machine change-over must be considered.

Layout of packaging lines must take into account the needs of the labour necessary for both operations and maintenance. With manual operation, ergonomic consideration of the working area, height of conveyors, seating, etc., must be given, to minimise fatigue and hence risk of errors. Placing and layout of machine controls or control panels also requires study (see *References 49–51*).

Sufficient area must be available for palletising of finished product where truck removal to warehouse is employed together with adequate access. Safety aspects of packaging must consider the safe working of the equipment, safeguarding of the operators, prevention of cross contamination of the product, and prevention of microbiological

Figure 52   *Packaging booths (by courtesy of ICI Ltd.)*

contamination. In safeguarding the product, spacing of packaging lines, need for screened areas and air conditioned rooms may well contribute to the packaging floor layout (see *Figure 52*).

References   See References 49–51 on Packaging.

2.5 Warehouse Storage

A warehouse can be split into five main sections:

1) Storage area.
2) Ancillary areas, e.g. prepacking
3) Preparation
4) Receiving
5) Despatching

The size of the storage area is principally determined by the required stockholding but is, so far as gangway space is concerned, affected by the throughput and the need to recover packages quickly. The remaining sections are mainly involved with preparation and their size is dependent on the throughput.

Solids can be stored in boxes, bags, barrels or drums. Liquids are contained in barrels, kegs, drums, cans or bottles, whilst gases are stored under pressure in heavy gauge cylinders. Before the storage area is determined, it has to be established how the packages are to be kept (i.e. whether on pallets) and the method of handling them to and from the store.

The warehouse should be arranged so that it is impossible to stack so high as to overload the floor. Items should be grouped so that they require similar fire fighting equipment. Toxic materials should be stored in a well ventilated area, especially if the containers are breakable. For hot or cold stores, the location of doors is important to prevent draughts. Petroleum and petroleum products having a flashpoint below 22°C must be stored in a building licensed under the Petroleum Spirit Regulations or in the open air in an area specially constructed to accommodate spillage.

Space must be left for vehicle packing during loading and offloading. 15m × 2.4m should be allowed for the vehicle with 4m space between and around each vehicle for fork lift truck access (see *Figure 53*).

Pallet racking systems utilise floor to a maximum whilst still allowing access to any individual item stored. A typical pallet size is 1.2m × 1.2m × 150mm high. Pallets are handled principally by fork lift trucks and overhead cranes. A turret truck will lift a load not exceeding 1Mg to a height of 7m and operate in narrower aisles of 2m

Figure 53   *Warehouse unloading point (by courtesy of ICI Ltd.)*

(see *Figure 53*). For larger loads a high reach fork lift truck can be used operating in aisles of 2.7m. Use of cranes is likely to result in a less flexible layout. Experience has shown that a figure of 80% pallet utilisation is reasonable for an efficiently run warehouse. An example of a conventional single racking system is shown in *Table 10*.

Many products are received, handled and despatched in large quantities. These are often stored in 'blocks', i.e. several pallets deep handled from a single aisle so that maximum use is made of the floor area. A system of 'live storage' may be used, in this case. This is a method of racking equipped with roller conveyors so that a number of pallets can be stored on one length of conveyor. The pallets are fed from one end and rolled to the other for withdrawal (see *Table 11*).

Figure 54   *Typical palletised store (by courtesy of ICI Ltd.)*

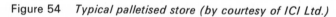

Table 10 *Example of conventional (single) racking*

Aisle	2.7m
Storage	2.4m
Aisle	2.7m
Storage	2.4m
Aisle	2.7m
Pallets stored 8 high 1.4m between pallet centres along storage rack.	

Table 11 *Example of live storage*

Aisle	2.7m
Storage 10 pallets deep	12m
Aisle	2.7m
Storage 11 Pallets deep	13.2m
Aisle	2.7m
Pallets stored 7 high 1.35m between pallet centres along storage rack.	

Table 12 *Example of outside palletised storage*

Aisle	4.0m
Storage	2.4m
Storage	2.4m
Aisle	4.0m
Storage	2.4m
Storage	2.4m
Aisle	4.0m

4 drums/pallet
4 pallets high
1.35m between pallet centres along
storage rack.

Certain items can be stored outside which is cheaper than covered storage. Examples of these are 0.4m^3 drums (*Table 12*). Items can be typically stored on pallets 4 high and handled by standard fork lift trucks capable of lifting 3Mg and operating in aisles of 4m width.

Unpalletised stores are usually serviced by electrically hand operated trucks for the smaller containers. The aisle should be wide enough for trucks $1\frac{1}{2}$ truck lengths (not widths), to manoeuvre. For large containers such as bags, overhead cranes may be used. In both cases the floor should be marked out into manageable lots for stock-taking purposes.

3 LAYOUT OF PIPEWORK

3.1 Pipes

3.1.1 Location

To provide ease of operation, to facilitate action during an emergency and to avoid unnecessary lengths of piping, plants and sections of plants should be arranged in process sequence. Utilities such as steam and water mains should in general be run parallel to the road system and should avoid going through the centre of a plant area. Within plant limits, piping should be run above ground, except that water or gas mains may be buried if considered necessary for safety, frost protection or economy. Piping run at ground level is cheaper than if elevated on supports, and is widely used in tank farms and for mains distribution but in the plant is liable to interfere with access. Within the plant, attempts should be made to route pipes adjacent to supporting structures like plant steelwork or walls, providing this is economical or does not affect the operation of the pipeline. Vertical pipes should be grouped and run through slots in plant floors, preferably near to stanchions, to facilitate support and to avoid weakening floor plates.

3.1.2 Buried Piping

To prevent freezing, water mains should be buried below the frost line or to a minimum of 750mm. Such lines should not run under process and service areas and where they go under roads and other concreted areas they should be laid in ducts or solidly encased in concrete.

Where valves, meters and similar fittings are used on buried piping they should be housed in a suitable brick or concrete chamber with proper access to the surface. Room must be allowed for anchors at pipe ends and changes of direction.

Buried gas piping should not be laid in plastic material or laid adjacent to potable water piping or plastic or asbestos materials.

Where buried lines are laid near to or across buried electric power cables they should always be laid beneath the cables. Pipes carrying hot liquids should be laid as far away from the cables as possible.

Buried water pipes servicing fire hydrants should be laid as ring mains to provide uniform pressure around the main. Fire mains should be located between the perimeter roads and the plant. The local Fire Authority should be consulted at an early stage regarding the layout of main, dry riser and hydrants.

Electric power, telephone cables etc., should be run in sand filled trenches covered by concrete tiles or a coloured concrete mix. These cables should, if possible be run at the high point of paving, leaving room for draw boxes.

If underground piping and cables are used, it is essential that the pipe and cable is put into position at the same time as foundation work is being undertaken.

3.1.3 Pipe Trenches

Open pipe trenches may be used in places where there is no risk of flammable vapours collecting or of the material freezing, e.g. for steam mains. They should not be used where there is a danger of flooding. It is often convenient to run open trenches alongside roadways at such an elevation that the pipes can run under the road with no change in elevation. The minimum width of pipe trenches should be 600mm. A minimum clearance of 100mm should be provided between pipe projections and walls and 50mm to the high point of trench bottoms.

3.1.4 Piping at Ground Level (Grade)

Piping at grade is the cheapest arrangement but within plant limits is liable to interfere with access. The pipes are normally placed on supports to raise them 300mm or more above the ground to permit easy cleaning and painting. Requirements for trapping and draining will frequently determine the support height. Where the crossing of walkways is unavoidable the lines should be provided with stiles.

3.1.5 Overhead Piping

Pipebridges, racks and supports should be of the simplest form with the minimum of cross bracing or infilling of steelwork to give the maximum freedom for pipe routing (see *Figure 55*). They should have sufficient space (say 30 %) and strength, to allow for extra pipework in future extensions. Every effort should be made to establish the number of pipes on a bridge before the steelwork design is too far committed. Pipes should be spaced to leave at least 25mm between the widest point of the pipes, and due allowance should be made for lagging (see *Table 13*).

To facilitate erection and to reduce bending moments on structural steel, large bore piping (e.g. cooling water and gas mains) should

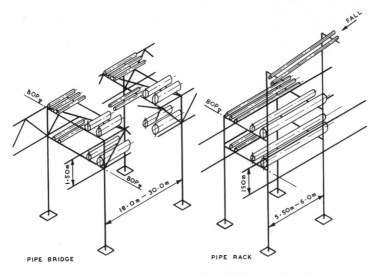

Figure 55   *Distances on pipe bridges and racks*

be located as close to the stanchions as possible. On the other hand steam mains should be run on the outside edge of the pipeway to permit the expansion loops to have the greatest width over the pipeway and to make it easier for loops to be nested. When utility and process lines share the same pipeway the former should be on the upper deck. Triple layer piping should be avoided.

Hot pipes and pipes carrying solvents should preferably not run adjacent to electric cables and pipe joints (excluding welded joints) should preferably not be located above roads, walkways and cable trays. (Only lines requiring complete drainage for process, corrosion or safety reasons should have a continuous slope.) These should be run on extensions of the structural steel, the extension being positioned at each stanchion to suit the fall (see *Figure 56*). The position of supports and a 'fall' should be such that fluid could not collect at the lowest point.

Take-off elevations from pipeways should be at a constant elevation consistent with the range of pipe sizes involved. However, headers should be located on the pipeway on that side from which the largest number of off-takes are made. Branch connections should normally be at 90° to the main pipe but may 'roll-off' at any convenient angle to minimise the length of pipe runs. Wherever banks of pipes change direction it is preferable to arrange for a change of elevation. This also

Table 13 Distance between centre lines of pipes in pipe-tracks and trenches for **1** and **2** MN/m²Class

NOM. PIPE SIZE (mm)	1 MN/m² A	1 MN/m² B	2 MN/m² A	2 MN/m² B
600	740	410	790	460
500	630	350	670	390
450	575	320	610	360
400	530	300	555	325
350	470	270	495	295
300	430	255	450	260
250	365	205	385	225
200	310	175	330	195
150	250	140	270	160
100	200	115	210	130
75	165	100	175	105
50	135	100	140	100
40	115	100	130	100

UNINSULATED LINES 1 MN/m CLASS CENTRE TO CENTRE (upper right) / UNINSULATED LINES 2MN/m² CLASS CENTRE TO CENTRE (lower left)

NOM. PIPE SIZE (mm)	600	500	450	400	350	300	250	200	150	100	75	50	40		NOM. PIPE SIZE (mm)
40	460	400	370	350	320	295	255	225	190	165	145	130	115	790	600
50	465	405	375	355	325	300	260	230	195	170	155	135	670	740	500
75	480	420	390	370	340	315	275	245	210	185	165	610	645	710	450
100	490	435	400	385	350	325	290	255	225	200	555	585	620	685	400
150	515	460	430	410	380	355	315	285	250	495	530	560	595	660	350
200	545	485	455	435	405	380	340	310	450	480	515	545	575	645	300
250	570	510	480	465	430	405	365	385	425	455	490	520	550	620	250
300	595	540	505	490	455	430	330	360	395	430	460	495	525	595	200
350	610	555	520	505	470	270	305	335	370	405	435	465	500	565	150
400	635	580	545	530	210	245	275	310	345	375	410	440	470	540	100
450	660	605	575	175	200	230	260	295	330	365	395	430	460	530	75
500	690	630	140	165	185	215	250	280	320	350	380	415	445	515	50
600	740	130	135	155	180	210	240	275	310	345	375	410	440	510	40
NOM. PIPE SIZE	3¾	5	7½	10	15	20	25	30	35	40	45	50	60		NOM. PIPE SIZE

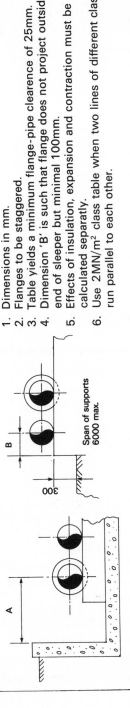

Span of supports
6000 max.

B

300

A

1. Dimensions in mm.
2. Flanges to be staggered.
3. Table yields a minimum flange-pipe clearence of 25mm.
4. Dimension 'B' is such that flange does not project outside end of sleeper but minimal 100mm.
5. Effects of insulation, expansion and contraction must be calculated separatly.
6. Use 2MN/m² class table when two lines of different class run parallel to each other.

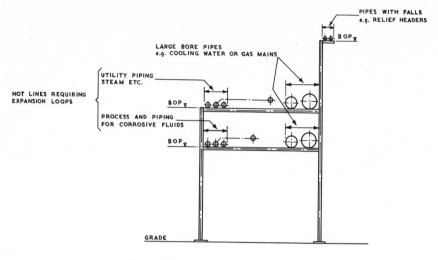

Figure 56   *Layout on pipe racks*

gives the opportunity to change the sequence of pipes and extend the piperack at a future date.

Minimum overhead clearances should be maintained to the underside of pipe, flange, lagging or support:

1) Above roads and areas with access for crane   —   7m
2) Plant areas where truck access required   —   4m
3) Plant areas general   —   3m
4) Above access floors and walkways within buildings —   2.25m
5) Above railway lines (top of rail)   —   4.6m

3.1.6 Maintenance

Piping arrangement should allow for removal of equipment for inspection or servicing. Maintenance areas provided in plant areas for mobile equipment access, tube bundle removal, etc., shall as far as possible be clear of piping. Horizontal piping supported in a vertical bank must be capable of having each pipe removed independently. Supports should be be provided where practicable so as to reduce the necessity for temporary supports in the following cases:

1) Where regular maintenance requires removal of equipment such as control valves, safety and relief valves and in line instruments.
2) Where lines must be dismantled for cleaning.

Special consideration must be given to the support and positioning of safety and relief valve discharge pipes. Except for steam tracing, pipes should normally not be supported from other pipes.

Piping requiring frequent (at least once a week) cleaning should be provided, at changes of direction, with flanged fittings or with bends of minimum radius 5 diameters. Cross pieces may be fitted instead of tees. 12m is the maximum length of pipe for single end cleaning and 24m for double end. Lines requiring infrequent cleaning should be provided with sufficient break flanges for dismantling and room must be left for removing the sections of pipe (see *Figure 57*).

Branches for hose connections for water, steam and air should be sited so that areas to be served can be reached with a 15m hose.

3.2 Pipe Fittings

3.2.1 Valves

A valve with a horizontal spindle is easiest to use when its hand-wheel spindle is between 750mm (small valves) and 1.5m (large valves) above the operating level (see *Figure 58*). The maximum height above the operating level of the spindle of a horizontally mounted valve should not normally exceed 2.1m. For valves mounted with the spindle vertical, the optimum height of the handwheel is approximately 1.1m above the operating level. If the valve is used infrequently heights up to

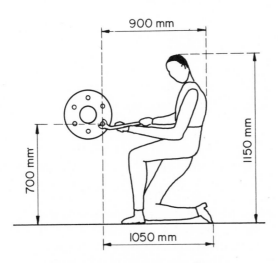

Figure 57   *Access to pipe flanges*

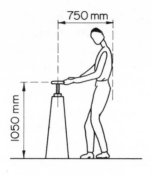

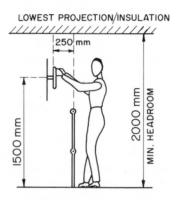

Figure 58   *Valve height*

1.5m are acceptable. (Valves should not be mounted in the inverted position because of the possibility of deposited solids getting into the gland). It is not good practice to locate valves which have to be operated regularly, such that they have to be reached from fixed or portable ladders. Wherever possible this practice should be avoided and only allowed if there is no reasonable alternative and the valve operation is only required occasionally (not more than once per month). Valves which are operated very rarely (say once per year) may be inaccessible to a process operator provided that no valves requiring to be operated in an emergency are located in such a position. If the spindle height of a horizontally mounted valve is more than 2.1m above the operating level a chain wheel should be provided. Such valves should be so located and orientated that the chains hang to within 1m of the operating level and do not foul access ways. The number of valves in this category should be kept to a minimum.

All relief valves, safety valves or bursting discs, discharging to atmosphere should be piped to safety. They should normally discharge at a height of 3m above the highest working level or building roof within a radius of 12m. Relief valves should discharge to a closed system when they release heavy hydrocarbon vapours having a molecular weight of 60 or more, toxic or lethal vapours and liquids, or flammable liquids.

Liquids which are not toxic, lethal or flammable may discharge to grade. No valve or restriction of any kind, excepting a bursting disc, is permissible between single relief valves and the equipment they are protecting. When twin relief valves are used, isolations must be provided before both relief valves in the form of two interlocked block valves so that one relief valve is always available for operation. Access to relief valves may be by fixed ladder for 75mm bore or smaller but preferably by platform or floor for larger ones. For maintenance purposes a hitching point or davit should be considered for larger valves, e.g. weighing over 9kg.

3.2.2 Control Valves and Instrument Detectors

Control valves and detectors such as temperature, pressure, level or flow devices which require infrequent attention can be reached by a short (2.5m) portable ladder. Those instruments requiring attention situated between 2.1m and 3.7m should be reached by fixed ladders, and, if above 3.7m by platforms. Other detectors such as pH, infra-red, GPC, refractive index which require frequent servicing, should be reached from the floor or a platform. For valves of instruments weighing more than 9kg a hitching point or davit should be considered unless near the floor when access should be left for a truck to be wheeled underneath. Control valves should normally be installed with their spindles vertical and for sizes 75mm N.B. and above should be mounted with at least 400mm clearance above the floor or access platform. Sufficient space must be allowed for the removal of control valves top works and bottom covers without removing the valve from the line.

3.2.3 Local Instruments

Instruments read on the plant such as temperature indicators, sight glasses level gauges, rotameters, pressure gauges should be at about eye height 1.7m for an operator standing on floor or platform (see *Figure 7*).

Hand regulating valves used together with locally mounted instruments should be located so that the instrument readings can be readily observed whilst operating the valves.

3.2.4 Sample Points

Ideally sample points should be about one metre off the floor, but if lower they should always be high enough to put the sample bottle etc., underneath (including the allowance for tundish). They should not be at eye level or above. Access is by platform or floor. It is desirable that sampling points should be grouped together and provided with adequate venting, drainage and access.

References

Computerised Layout of Plant

1 ARMOUR, G. C, BUFFA, E. S. and VOLLMAN, T. E. Allocating facilities with CRAFT. *Harvard Business Review.* **42**, (2). 1964.
2 BUSH, M. J. and WELLS, G. L. Computer Aided Production of Unit Plot Plans for Chemical Plant. *IChemE Symposium Ser.* **35** 2 : 15. 1972.
3 EVANS, W. O. Automated Layout Design Programe. *IBM Corporation.*
4 GUNN, J. D. The Optimised Layout of a Chemical Plant by Digital Computer. *Computer Aided Design.* 2 (3). 111. 1970.
5 LEE, R. C. and MOORE, J. M. Corelap—Computerised Relationship Layout Planning. *Journal of Industrial Engineering.* **XVIII** (3). 1967.
6 LEESLEY, M. E. and NEWELL, R. G. The Determination of Plant Layout by Interactive Computer Methods. *IChemE Symposium Ser.* **35** 2 : 20. 1972.
7 MUNTHER, R. D. Systematic Layout Planning. *Industrial Education Institute,* Boston, 1961.
8 REED, R. Plant Location, Layout and Maintenance. *Richard D. Irwin Inc.* 1967.

Cryogenic Plant Layout

9 BRITISH CRYOGENICS COUNCIL. *Cryogenic Safety Manual.* London 1970.

Effluent

10 SEPPA, W. D. Fundamentals of Sewer Design. *Hydro Proc. & Pet Ref.* **43** (10) 171. 1964.

Electrical Distribution

11 BRITISH STANDARDS INSTITUTION. Electrical Apparatus in Explosive Atmosphere. C. P. 1003. London 1963–7.
12 HMSO ELECTRICITY FACTORY ACTS. Special Regulations. 1908 and 1944. London
13 INSTITUTE OF ELECTRICAL ENGINEERS. IEE Regulations. London
14 SILVERMAN, D. Electrical Design, part 1 Distribution. *Chem. Eng.* **71**, 131. 1964

Electrochemical Plant Layout

15 HARDIX, D. W. F. Electrical Manufacture of Chemicals from Salt. *Oxford University Press.* 1959.

16 HINE F. The Optimum Number of Cells in an Amalgam Process Chlorine Plane. *Electrochemical Technology.* **117**, 139. 1970.

Enclosed Buildings and Control Room Layout

17 BRITISH STANDARDS INSTITUTION. Electrical Apparatus in Explosive Atmospheres. CP1003, London 1963–7.

18 EDWARDS, E., AND LEES, F. P. Man-Computer Interaction in Process Control. *IChemE* London. 1973

19 HMSO ELECTRICITY (FACTORY ACTS) Special Regulations 1908 and 1944.

20 ENGINEERING EQUIPMENT USERS ASSOCIATION Handbook No. 7 Factory Steel Stairways, Ladders and Handrails. London 1962.

Explosion Relief

21 FIRE PROTECTION ASSOCIATION. Technical Information Sheet 3012. London 1966.

22 FIRE RESEARCH NOTE 787. Fire Protection Engineering with particular reference to Chemical Engineering. Fire Research Station. Borehamwood.

23 GRAVINER (COLNBROOK) LTD. Explosion Protection and Suppression for Industry. Slough 1966

24 MINISTRY OF LABOUR. Dust Explosions in factories *New Series. No. 22, HMSO.* London 1963.

25 MINISTRY OF LABOUR. Guide to the use of Flame Arrestors and Explosion Reliefs. *New Series. No. 34, HMSO.* London 1965.

Explosions in Cyclones

26 FIRE RESEARCH NOTE NO. 639. The Expolosibility of some Industrial Dusts in a large scale Cyclone Plant. *Fire Research Station, Borehamwood.*

Gas Pressure Storage

27 BRITISH CRYOGENICS COUNCIL. Cryogenics Safety Manual. London 1970.

28 HMSO. The Highly Flammable Liquids Regulations. Factories Act London 1961.

29 ICI LIMITED. Engineering Codes and Regulations. *Liquified Flammable Gases—Storage and Handling.* London 1970.

30 INSTITUTE OF GAS ENGINEERS. Publication I.G.E./SR 6 London.

31 INSTITUTE OF PETROLEUM—Model Codes of Safe Practice in the Petroleum Industry. London 1956.
32 SHELL MEX AND BP GASES LIMITED. Liquified Petroleum for Installation. London.

General Layout
33 EVANS, H. P. Plant Layout, the first step towards low cost. *Ref. Eng.* C14. March 1960.
34 GOETZ, M. M. Plant Layout *Kirk-Othmer Encyclopedia of Chemical Technology 2nd ed.* **15** 689–599. Interscience. 1968. (14 references not duplicated here)
35 HOUSE, F. F. An Engineers Guide to Process Plant Layout. *Chem. Eng.* 76, 120. 28th July, 1969.
36 KAESS, D. Trouble Free Plant Layout. *Chem. Eng.* June 1st 1970.
37 MC GARRY, J. F. A check list for Plant Layout. *Pet. Ref. 37* (10) 109, 1958.
38 SACHS, G. Economics and Technical Factors in Chemical Plant Layout. *The Chem. Eng. 242* CE304, (Oct. 1970).

Heat Exchanger Layout
39 KERN, R. How to Design Heat Exchanger Piping. *Pet. Ref. 39* (2), 137. 1960.

Layout Techniques
40 BRITISH STANDARDS INSTITUTION. Site Investigations. *CP 2001.* London 1957.
41 MACKENZIE, G. The Time and Resource Aspects of Project management in the Construction of Chemical Plants. *The Chem. Eng.* London 208. CE118 June 1967.
42 ELLIOT, E. M. and OWEN, J. M. Critical Examination in Process Design. *The Chem. Eng.* 223. CE377 Nov. 1968.
43 MUTHER, R. Systematic layout planning. *Industrial Education Institute.* Boston 1961.

Models for Plant Layout
44 BIDDLE, K. and WANDERMAN, H. Engineering Design Models for Chemical and Petroleum Plants. *Petroleum* 30 *(2) 49,* 1967.
45 BIDDLE, K. and WANDERMAN, H. The Case for Design Models. *Gas Journal.* Oct. 12th 1966.
46 BRITISH STANDARD INSTITUTION. Specification of Identification of Pipe lines. *CP 1710* London 1960.
47 BUSH, M. J. and WELLS, G. L. Unit Plot Plans for Plant Layout. *British Chem. Eng.* 16, 325, 514. 1971.

48 NATIONAL ENGINEERING LABORATORY. Modern aids to Design and Draughting *Report No. 347*. Glasgow 1968.

Packaging
49 FIELDS, A. Method Study. (Especially Chapter 9.) *Cassel*, London 1969.
50 KELLERMAN, F., *et alia*. Ergonomics in Industry. *Phillips Technical Library*. Eindhoven 1963.
51 MAYNARD, H. M. (ed) Industrial Engineering Handbook. *2nd edition McGraw-Hill*, N.Y. 1963.

Pneumatic Conveying
52 ENGINEERING EQUIPMENT USERS ASSOCIATION. Handbook No. 15. Pneumatic handling of powdered materials. *Constable and Company*, London 1963.

Radioactive Plant Layout
53 Proceedings of the 3rd International Conference on the Peaceful Uses of Atomic Energy, Geneva. 10, 233, 1964.
54 Information is available from the UKAEA'S Health and Safety Branch, Risley, Lancs.

Safe Distances
55 YELLAND, A. E. J. Design Considerations when Assessing Safety in Chemical Plants. *The Chem. Eng.* 201 CE214 (1966).

Safety
56 BRITISH STANDARDS INSTITUTION. Electrical Apparatus in Explosive Atmospheres. *CP 1003*. London 1963–7.
57 CRYOGENICS SAFETY MANUAL, British Cryogenics Council. London 1970.
58 HMSO FACTORIES ACT, London 1961.
59 INSTITUTE OF PETROLEUM. Model Codes of Safe Practice in the Petroleum Industry. London 1956.
60 JENNET, E. Safety in Structural Design Layout and Piping. *The Chem. Eng.* 71, 207. 14th Sept. 1964.
61 LINDMAN, P. F. Safety and Fire Protection Today. *Hydro Process*, 44 (4) 125. 1965.
62 PREEDY, D. L. Guidelines for Safety and Loss Prevention. *Chem. Eng.* 76, 94, 21st April 1969.
63 RASBASH, D. J. Fire Protection Engineering with Particular Reference to Chemical Engineering. *The Chem. Eng.* 243 CE 385. 1970 (see CE388/9 and references).

64 SIMPSON, H. G. Design for Loss Prevention—Plant Layout. *I.Chem. E. Symposium Ser* 34 105. 1971.

65 WILSON, R. Here's Protection Monsanto Style. *Hydroc. Process.* 43 (4) 185. 1964.

66 YELLAND, A. E. J. Design Considerations when Assessing Safety in Chemical Plant. *The Chem. Eng.* 201 CE214, 1966. (classifies various codes of practice).

Site Location

67 ANON. Picking a Plant site by Digital Computer. *The Chem. Eng.* 71. 88, 20 Jan. 1964.

68 BIERWERT, D. V. and KRONE, F. A. How to Find the Best Site for New Plant. *The Chem. Eng.* 62 191, Dec. 1955.

69 CREMER, H. W. The Siting and Layout of Industrial Works. *Trans. Inst. Chem. Eng.*, 23, 52 (1945).

70 GRAY, J. Physical Aspects of Plant Site Selection, *Chem. Eng. Prg.* 56 (11) 46 (1960).

71 KALTENECKER, L. V. Plant Location. *Kirk-Othmer Encyclopedia of Chemical Technology* 2nd Ed. **15** 700–719 Interscience, N.Y. 1968. (33 references not duplicated here).

72 MOHLMAN, F. W. Waste Disposal as a Factor in Plant Location. *Chem. Eng. Prog.*, 46 (7) 321, 1950.

73 MURDOCK, Selection of Site for Chemical Factory. *The Chem. Eng.* 31, 1196. Aug. 5 1961.

Storage

74 HOUSE, F. F. Engineers Guide to Plant Layout. *The Chem. Eng.* 76 120. 28th July, 1969.

75 INSTITUTE OF PETROLEUM. Model Codes of Safety Practice in the Petroleum Industry. London 1956.

Trough Belt Conveyors

76 MECHANICAL HANDLING ENGINEERS ASSOCIATION. Recommended Practice for Troughed Belt Conveyors. London 1962.

INDEX TO CLEARANCES, SIZES ETC.

Administration buildings,
  clearances around, 56
Aisles,
  width,
    container warehouses, 122, 123
    conveyors, 98, 99
    filters, 82
    general, 23
    pumps, 79

Barometric legs, (see appropriate item)
Bulk solid storage, (see Storage)
Bursting discs, (see Valve relief)

Canteen,
  area, 56
  clearances, 57
Central buildings,
  area, 56
  clearances, 57
Central services,
  boiler, clearances from other items, 57
  cooling towers
    area, 56
    clearances from other items, 57
  effluent plant,
    clearances from other items, 57
    vent safety distances, 9
Centrifuges,
  access around, 58, 86
Columns,
  base height, 73
  clearances between adjacent, 58, 75
  clearances between adjacent platforms,
    75
  internal access, minimum diameter, 74
    ladder dimensions, 74
  manhole dimensions, 74
  maximum length of sections, 74

packing storage, 59
platform support, minimum diameter
    and shell thickness for, 73
self support, minimum diameter for,
    73
Compressors,
  access around, 59, 81
Container storage (see Storage,
    warehouse)
Control panel (see Instrument panel)
Control room,
  dimensions, 27
Control valve (see Valve, control)
Conveyors,
  fluidised,
    angle, 99
    cross section vs. capacity, 100
  mechanical,
    angle, 98, 112
    belt take-up, 98
    belt width, 98, 99
    clearances between, 98, 99
    walkway width and height, 98, 99
Cooling towers,
  area, 56
Crushers,
  clearances around, 58

Dryers,
  access around, 58, 87

Evaporators,
  barometric leg height, 70
  platform height, 70
  stagger angle, 70
Exchangers,
  clearance between adjacent, 76
  clearance for bundle removal, 59, 76
  height above ground, 59, 77

Filters,
    batch filter,
        access around, 59, 84
        elevation, 59
        stagger angle, 84
    rotary vacuum filter,
        access around, 59, 86
        barometric leg height, 85
        elevation, 59
Fire stations
    areas, 56
    clearances around, 57
Flanges,
    access, 128
Floors
    area for catalyst removal, 66
    number of exits, 23
    slope around pumps, 80
    spacing, 22
Furnaces
    clearances between adjacent, 58, 72
    clearances from other equipment, 57,
        58, 72
    clearance from wall, 58
    distance from drain manholes, 72
    height of base, 73
    peephole height, 73
    platform size, 73

Garages
    area, 56
    clearances around, 57
Gas storage (see Storage, gas)

Instruments
    detectors, access and height, 132
    local, optimum height, 27, 132
    panel, access around, 26
        optimum height, 26, 27

Laboratories
    central,
        area, 56
        clearance around, 57
    local,
        dimensions, 27
Ladders
    angle, clearance and dimensions, 23,
        24
    maximum height, 23, 74

    safety hoops and cage requirements,
        23, 74
Liquid storage (see Storage, liquid)
Loading areas
    distance to other items, 57
    size for liquids, 103
    size for solids, 121

Medical centres
    area, 56
    clearances around, 57
Mills
    clearances around, 58
Mixers
    access around, 58
Models
    block,
        minimum pipe size, 45
        scale, 45
    cut-out
        scale, 43
    piping,
        cost, 50
        minimum pipe size, 50
        scale, 50

Paths
    distance to buildings, 57
    headroom, 57
    width, 56
Paved areas
    headroom, 57
    slope, 9
Pipes
    access for cleaning, 130
    access to flanges, 130
    at grade, height, 9, 129
    bridges,
        dimensions, 128
        headroom, 9, 128, 129
        oversizing, 8, 125
    clearances, 8, 125, 126
    maximum hose length, 130
    racks, headroom, 22, 128
    trenches, dimensions, 8, 125
Plant areas
    distance to other areas, 22, 57
    headroom, 129
    height and safety, 15
Platforms
    area,

catalyst removal, 66
    columns, 73
    evaporators, 70
  height when required, 22
  maximum length of ladder between, 74
  number of exits, 22
Pumps
  aisle width, 79
  clearances between, 79
  clearances with other items, 59, 79
  door dimensions for rooms, 79
  floor slope, 80
  lifting beams,
    clearance for, 80
    minimum weight for, 79
    plinth height and slope, 80
  shelter,
    frequency of use, 78
    dimensions, 79
Starter height, 81
  suction, length of straight run, 79

Railways
  distance to buildings, etc., 57, 110
  curve, 56
  headroom, 57, 129
Reactors
  access around, 58
  catalyst removal,
    free floor area, 66
    platform area, 66
Roads
  distance to buildings etc., 57, 110
  headroom, 57, 129
  tanker details, 104, 105
  width, 56

Sample points
  height, 133
Screens
  angle, 94
Stacks
  distance to other items, 57
Stairways
  angle clearances and dimensions, 23, 24
  maximum height without landing, 23
  number required, 23
Steps
  maximum height, 23
Stirred vessels
  access around, 58

Storage
  bulk solid,
    cantilever, maximum length, 112
    closed warehouse dimensions, 117
    conveyor angle, 112
    open pile dimensions, 116
    tripper support distance, 114
  gas and pressure,
    clearances to other items, 57, 59, 109,
      110
    spacings, 59, 109, 110
  liquid,
    anti-spillage wall height, 106
    bunds capacity, 106, 107
      height of concrete, 106
      shape of earth, 106
    flashpoint classification, 103
    group capacities, 107
    loading island dimensions, 103
    road tanker details, 104, 105
    spacings, 59, 106
  warehouse, container,
    aisles, width of, 122, 123
    distance to other buildings, 57
    drum storage, 122, 123
    fork lift height, 122
    live storage clearances, 123
    open storage clearances, 123
    pallet sizes, 122
    single racking clearances, 123
    vehicle unloading space, 121

Tanks (see Storage, liquid)

Valves
  access, 131, 132
  clearances, 132
  davits, minimum weight for, 132
  frequency of access, 131
  height, need for chain, 131
  optimum height, 130, 131
  relief and safety, discharge distances,
    132
Vents
  safe discharge distances, 9, 132

Warehouses (see Storage, bulk solid and
    container)
Welding
  safe distance, 21
Workshops
  clearances from other buildings etc., 57

SUBJECT INDEX

Access (see appropriate item)
Acid plants, 101
Administration buildings, 10
After coolers, 90
Air cooled exchangers, 77
Air filters, 95
Ambulance station, 12
Analogues for layout, 43
Appearance, 20
Autoclaves, 64

Ball mill reactors, 64
Ball mills as crushers, 91
Barometric legs (see appropriate item)
Batch filters, 83
Batch reactors, 64
Belt conveyors, 98, 112
Block models, 45
Boilers, 7, 101
Bucket conveyors, 98, 112
Buildings, choice of, 21
Bulk solids storage, 109
Buried piping, 124
Bursting discs, 132

Canteens, 10
Catalytic reactors, 65
Centrifugal compressors, 81
Centrifuges, 86
Chute conveyors, 84, 85, 97
Clearances (see index to clearances)
Closed warehouses, 113
Columns, 73
Compressors, 81
Computers, 53
Constructional considerations, 18
Container storage, 120
Continuous filters, 84
Control room, 25
Control valves, 132

Conveyor driers, 88
Conveyors, 98
Cooling towers, 7
Correlation and compatibility techniques, 35
Crushers, 91
Cryogenic plant, 101
Crystallisers, 71
Cut-outs, 43
Cyclones, 95

Development of layout, 28, 29
Drag link conveyors, 98, 112
Drawings, 46
Drum storage, 120
Dryers, 86

Economical considerations, 15
Effluent plant, 9
Electrochemical plant, 101
Emergency services, 12
Enclosed buildings, 23
Environmental aspects, 13
Evaporators, 70
Exchangers, 75

Fans, 82
Filling equipment, 118
Filters, air, 95
    liquid/solid, 83
Fire stations, 12
Fired equipment, 72
Fixed bed reactors, 65
Floors, (see also appropriate item) 22
Fluid transfer equipment, 78
Fluidised bed conveyors, 98
Fluidised bed reactors, 66
Furnaces, 72
Future expansion, 21

Garages, 10
Gas-solid contractors, 86
Gas storage, 109
Geographical factors, 14
Ground level piping, 125

Headroom (see particular item)
Height (see particular item)

Inert gas generators, 101
Initial development of layout, 29
Instruments, 25, 132

Laboratories, central, 11
    plant, 25
Ladders, (see also appropriate item) 23
Line filters and strainers, 83
Liquid mixers, 69
Liquid storage, 102
Live container storage, 122
Loading areas, liquid, 103
    Container, 122

Maintenance considerations, (see also
    appropriate item) 18
Manholes, (see under appropriate item)
Material transportation, 6
Matrix exchanger, 78
Mechanical conveyors, 98
Medical centres, 10
Mills, 91
Mixers, 68
Models, 45, 50
Moving bed reactors, 66
Multi-product reactors, 65
Multi-product storage, 109

Nuclear plant, 101

Offices, plant, 25
    site, 10
Open pile storage, 111
Open structures, 22
Operational considerations, 18
Overhead piping, 125

Packaged plants, 101
Packaging equipment, 118
Packed tube reactors, 64
Palletised storage, 121
Panel control, 26

Parking areas, 11
Paste mixers, 68
Paths, 11
Pipe fittings, 130
Pipes, 122
Piping models, 50
Plant layout in general, 15
Plant vessels, 63
Pneumatic conveyors, 98
Power stations, 7
Precipitators, air, 95
Pressure storage, 109
Process considerations, 17
Proximity and sequencing, 42
Pump and switch houses, 8
Pumps, 78

Railways, 12
Reactors, 63
Reciprocating compressors, 81
Recovery plants, 101
Refrigeration plants, 101
Relief valves, 132
Roads, 11
Rotary dryers, 89
Rotary vacuum filters, 84

Safety considerations, 16
Safety valves, 132
Sample points, 133
Screens, 94
Sequence of activities, 28
Service distribution, 8
Sewers, 9
Shelter for pumps, 78
Silos, 113
Site layout, general, 3
Solid mixers, 68
Spacings (see appropriate item)
Specialised plants, 101
Spinning machines, 101
Spray driers, 88
Stacks, 10, 72
Stairways, 23
Starters for pumps, 80
Steps, 23
Storage, 102
Stores, central, 10
Switch rooms, 8, 26

Tabletting machines, 101